Journeying together

accompanying people living with dementia

Published by Redemptorist Publications
Wolf's Lane, Chawton, Hampshire, GU34 3HQ, UK
Tel. +44 (0)1420 88222, Fax. +44 (0)1420 88805
Email customercare@rpbooks.co.uk
www.rpbooks.co.uk

A registered charity limited by guarantee
Registered in England 03261721

First published February 2023

Edited by Sr Janet Fearns FMDM
Designed by Peena Lad

ISBN 978-0-85231-626-9

A CIP catalogue record for this book is available from the British Library

Printed by Bishops Printers, Portsmouth, PO6 1TR

Journeying together

accompanying people living with dementia

Joseph D. Cortis & Pia Matthews

redemptorist
publications

Contents

Foreword

Rt Rev. Marcus Stock, Bishop of Leeds

Caritas Leeds was launched in September 2017. Its motto is "Faith through loving service". One of its aims is to "provide a strong and coherent voice at the service of the bishop, on important social issues and policies for the Diocese of Leeds". This aim resulted in the setting up of several groups which would lead in providing resources to help existing parish groups in their ministry of charity and social action and also in identifying unmet needs. One group has a specific focus on dementia.

There are many significant challenges for people who live with dementia, not only those who personally live with the condition, but also for their families, carers and the clergy who minister to them. These challenges affect our parishes and communities. However, the presence of dementia in our society also offers all of us an opportunity to reflect on human dignity and the sanctity of life from conception to its natural end.

A key feature of this book is that it is based on listening to the testimonies of those living with the various stages of dementia and of those who care for them. Such voices may not often be heard due to a lack of awareness about dementia, negative stereotyping and discrimination or a general fear of this complex medical condition. As a result, there have been few opportunities to capture, listen and take actions based on people's testimonies.

The approach taken by this book is timely as it coincides with a worldwide listening process which the Catholic Church is currently undertaking from 2021 to 2024 through its Synodal Pathway (Journeying Together) and a Listening Church initiative. The methodology resonates with the call of Pope Francis for a more inclusive Church and is also integral to the spiritual mission of our parishes and Church communities.

I am pleased therefore to endorse this initiative and collaboration between the Dementia Group of Caritas Leeds and Dr Pia Matthews from St Mary's University, Twickenham. I believe that this book offers a practical, ethical and spiritual guide for those living with dementia and their carers, and also for clergy, Religious and lay faithful in how to make our parishes more inclusive and supportive. Living our faith through loving service is to put our faith into action. Each chapter therefore offers the reader prompts for a personal reflection which may well lead to a review of current practices or generate new initiatives and approaches.

Chapter 1

Voicing our story

Our book *Journeying Together* is written by people who have worked with and ministered to people with dementia and their families. However, we think that it is vital that the voices of people with dementia are there from the beginning. Certainly, as Tom Kitwood, a pioneer in dementia care, once said, "If you've met one person with dementia, you've met one person with dementia." Nevertheless, if we want to accompany people living with dementia, their families, friends and carers, then we need to listen to their experiences. These voices constantly inform the book. They ask challenging questions and they keep us all grounded in the realities of living fully with dementia. We recognise the ups and downs of the journey to becoming dementia-friendly, a journey that is not always easy and we chart what we have learned on the way. But there are also many moments of joy as we travel.

In this chapter we begin with five stories of experiences that we are sure will strike a chord with many people. Each is different and presented in varying forms: after all, no two people are the same.

The stories

The first, Maggie's story, is seen from the perspective of friends in a parish and it is perhaps a reminder that we are all unsure about dementia and how to help.

The second story is a chat between Andrea and one of the Caritas Leeds accompanying team. Andrea's experience gives us an indication of some of the losses which people with dementia experience.

In our third story Maureen speaks about how she and her husband live with dementia and we also hear from their grandchildren and daughter. We will hear more from Maureen later when she explains the experiences of the family during the covid pandemic.

We have set out the fourth story, where Joan's daughter-in-law looks back and forwards in stages so that we can ask some basic questions.

Looking back at your experience, what advice did you need?

- *What advice would you give yourself?*
- *What resources did you need?*
- *What did the person with dementia need?*

We have asked these questions because this book is not only about listening to the voices of people with dementia, and their family and carers. We hope to be able to learn from people's experiences so that this book can give practical advice on how to accompany people effectively.

In the fifth story, where we look at the practicalities facing family and carers, Rhoda talks about visiting her father Malcolm.

In the final section of this chapter, we have presented some reflections from the Caritas Leeds Dementia Group on their work of accompaniment. Their voices and those of people whom they have accompanied help to frame some of the issues that will be unpacked in the rest of the book.

Voices of people with dementia, their friends and families

Maggie's story – a parish perspective

"Maggie was a recently retired, secondary school maths teacher who had been very able and respected by pupils and teachers alike. On retirement, her involvement in the children's liturgy at Sunday Mass became an important part of her week. Maggie and her husband have five grown-up children.

Maggie was initially irritated by her gradual loss of memory: forgetting her handbag or where she was meant to be going. She had started a Mothers Prayers group in the parish but soon realised that she was no longer able to take on the necessary administration.

An accurate diagnosis of Maggie's Alzheimer's only came after a misdiagnosis of a brain tumour. The error, although serious, gave her some relief: it was tangible and gave Maggie a sense of knowing with what she was dealing. She was very upset, however, when this diagnosis was revised to Alzheimer's.

Maggie came to the weekly meetings of the Mothers Prayers group but would frequently lose her place in the prayer book and had to be shown the right page. When she stopped coming, she said that she had hated being unable to follow the prayers in the book and having someone point it out.

We were a very small group – six at the most. Maggie had appeared to enjoy and join in the chat before our meeting. Everyone loved Maggie and tried to help her feel part of the group. Someone would give her a lift to the meeting. Going home was different: she had a mobile phone and insisted on walking to the town centre, where she would phone her husband.

We were concerned that she was becoming more vulnerable, perhaps not safe to be out alone. It is hard not to appear to patronise such a highly intelligent, capable person and to understand the progress of the illness."

Andrea's experience – a sense of loss as life changes

1 What are you proud of in your life?

"I looked after my grandparents and parents well and didn't turn my back on them when the going got tough. My mother was bipolar and had other mental health issues.

Thinking about my strengths, I'm caring, compassionate and empathetic – these traits help you to relate to others with dementia and to understand the daily challenges of living with dementia. I'm good at helping friends, being supportive and go out of my way to support and help them with their problems. I'm very articulate.

My job in market and health research involved persuading people to take part in health studies, most of which were very personal and highly confidential. The specific skills needed to do this job are very demanding, often causing you to get upset and emotional. I always had to remain professional and not show emotion. It was a tightrope balance – the amount of questioning needed discretion."

2 Since you have been diagnosed with dementia, what has changed for you?

"I don't read anymore as am unable to recall what I have read. I have lost confidence and am more nervous. For example, I have given up driving – which has been a wrench. I chose to stop as I do not want to risk causing an accident.

I must be more mindful when I do anything and I can't do anything quickly or rush. I need to take my time with showering and getting dressed. I have no deadlines. I have lost my independence and the confidence to go off and do things on my own – such as going for a walk – that previously I would have done without thinking. I am fearful of slipping in the bath whereas previously this would not have been an issue.

Processing information can be difficult and causes immense fatigue and anxiety.

Having to move to sheltered accommodation from the family home and its familiarity makes me anxious. The world has closed in and is narrower and I lack confidence. I worry about having to rely on others to guide me. I'm more limited in what I can do and can't go off on my own. It is very constraining as I've always been a dynamo.

Dementia has caused me to neglect communicating with friends and instigating the communication. It has also stopped me from being able to do my personal washing and food shopping."

3 What support has been helpful to you?
"Friends looking out for me and including me in outings. They adjust their arrangements to include me. Also helpful have been peer group support, the online *Living with Dementia* course and opportunities to share strategies and experiences with people you relate to who are in the same boat. Helpful next-door neighbours, who do things like putting out the bins, have shown they are aware of my situation. They are very kind and look out for me. I am aware of other neighbours in the street who have offered to help with shopping and other activities."

4 What advice would you give others living with dementia?
"Trust those who offer to help and support you. Be selective, however, as to whom you can trust and confide in when asking for support or telling them you have dementia. People can take advantage of this, especially, perhaps, in a shop. For example, I was charged for items I had not purchased. This incident has vastly contributed to sapping my confidence. Slow down and don't be pressurised by others."

5 What advice would you give yourself now?
"I would give myself permission to be mindful and take my time, without rushing or panicking. It's important not to go somewhere on my own."

Maureen - living with a loved one with dementia

"Following my husband Mike's diagnosis of mixed dementia [more than one type of dementia] in 2012, change was inevitable. The areas which needed to be considered and addressed were practical, emotional and physical.

In order to deal with the practical changes required, it is important to understand the starting point.

Mike was a quietly spoken, professional, hands-on person who dealt with every practical matter in family life. He taught both me and our two children to drive, designed our garden from a blank canvas and was unflappable with every practical task. Gradually each aspect has been eroded and his confidence dealt bitter blows every time something else must be taken away.

Mike enjoyed many sporting activities. He played golf, danced, lectured for fourteen years, ran a post office, drove to work throughout the UK and completed every DIY job possible.

Despite many changes and challenges, Mike does not complain or argue with the things I plan for our entertainment and rarely contributes any suggestions.

Emotionally, it has been equally difficult. Mike still does not fully understand the complexity of his condition. He has a positive attitude on diagnosis and that continues to date. He is detached from the day-to-day running of life.

As Mike's carer, I have had to put his emotional needs first always in sensitive, tactful and patient ways. This is further complicated because, during our forty-six-year marriage, he has rarely shared his innermost emotions. This has just been exacerbated with the onset of dementia. I occasionally cry when times get hard. However, we are people of Christian faith and know we are not coping alone.

Physically, I handle everything now. Financially, I have Power of Attorney and handle the day-to-day running of the home, plan social activities, remember dates, birthdays and appointments. On an average day I put out Mike's clothes, oversee his dressing and washing, and make plans for the day's activities ahead.

I have sourced a day centre where qualified staff entertain and challenge Mike's memory alongside other dementia day guests. Together we still attend two walking groups and cover around thirteen miles weekly. We go to a weekly dance class and attend a monthly Alzheimer's Society Singing for the Brain group which we both enjoy.

How did we as a family feel about the diagnosis? Prior to the dementia diagnosis, many tests were completed over a nine-month period because Mike was under sixty-five years old. As each test result came through, I made our daughter and son aware of the results. When the time came to set up Power of Attorney, they were both involved.

When we were given the diagnosis, the consultant asked Mike if he felt suicidal! He did not and hasn't felt in the least depressed at any point.

Neither he nor I understood the severity or ramifications of that initial diagnosis in 2012. We were bright, healthy, active people and although we knew the theory surrounding the condition, we never thought it would be very serious for Mike. We were both at that stage in denial. He never thought the day would come when he could not drive, look after himself or lead a full and independent life. From my perspective, I thought that if I did everything I could to keep him active, busy, happy and fulfilled, the condition would not deteriorate and, for a couple of years, it didn't. I can recall being invited to attend a carers' course. Some people had a partner or parent who were housebound – Mike was on the golf course! We told our children the diagnosis at the outset and they were obviously upset. But again, it didn't seem real.

At first, I tried to shield the grandchildren from the diagnosis and I now feel that was incorrect. I can recall an instance when our elder grandsons and Mike were at the cinema together. Mike went to the toilet during the show and did not return. Our daughter and I were blissfully unaware until we came to collect them, at which point the distraught boys told us what had happened. The cinema staff went through all the screenings and found Mike in a completely different film, quite happy and unaware of the confusion. On another occasion our youngest grandson was troubled that Grandpa kept scoring at football for the other team! So, with hindsight, I should have confided in them earlier.

How do I and the family cope?

Today, we all care for Mike in the best way we can. He is included in everything and reminders of past times are shared frequently. Family photographs are displayed in our lounge and I often see Mike looking at them and naming each person. Our family play field games together and rounders is a great favourite. As a Liverpool football club supporter, our son once arranged tickets for the director's box at Anfield so that they could see Louis Suarez play. The event was a great success, although since then, Mike has not followed the team at all.

As well as a supportive family, we are fortunate to have a large group of friends who include us both in all events we choose to attend. We play many games, particularly football, badminton and table tennis – and allowances are made around the rigidity of any game rules! A close friend took Mike to Twickenham to see the Rugby World Cup and although the event was a success, he has mentioned that, given the decline in Mike's health, he doesn't feel able to do so alone again. Another friend watches golf on TV with Mike and despite efforts to stimulate a conversation, it was only when Mike had the opportunity to demonstrate a "skill" that Mike became engaged and animated.

Thinking about challenges, Mike has difficulty putting tasks into the correct order so, for example, when dressing he can mix day and nightwear items. Sometimes he leaves without advising me where he is going. We went on pilgrimage to Lourdes and when Mike left our bedroom, despite it only being two minutes afterwards when I left to see where he was, it took three and a half hours for the police to locate him in a different town 10km away.

Mike cannot retain advice, instructions or information now and I must give repeated guidance, gently emphasising the specific action required to complete the task. If we are travelling by car and there is anything to carry or load, Mike can become very confused and often puts the item back in its original place. He frequently changes his footwear in the house, whether slippers or shoes. He collects and arranges random items like combs, pens, oranges, apparently without reason. Mike never loses his temper or becomes anxious. He is sometimes frustrated and says he doesn't know what I want. At such moments, I prioritise the necessity for the task and leave it for another time if it is not essential.

I am very sociable and rely hugely on the companionship of family and groups of friends. This dynamic makes all the difference to the otherwise comparatively quiet and potentially lonely days.

Mike also enjoys a variety of companions and diversions. We love to sing, in the car, at church – anywhere! He remembers everyone's names and all the words to any song or hymn even though he can find it tough to think of the correct words to use in conversation.

Thinking about the future, dementia is like going on a train journey where you do not know either the destination or when and how you will alight from the train. We must simply make the best of the journey as the train travels along.

Nowadays, the closest Mike gets to feeling low is frustration when he is tired or doesn't understand what is required of him. On an average day, we wake snuggled in bed with Mike's arm draped across me and, for those few minutes, I remember how life was before his diagnosis of dementia. Once we rise, I select Mike's clothes for him and put them on the bed while I prepare breakfast. Mike will look around the rooms in the house and then sit quietly waiting until I bring in the tray. I will pass him his items for bathing, showering and dressing in his preferred order while making general conversation about what the day holds for us.

Despite this very challenging year, nothing on the news has touched Mike: he is oblivious to the outside world. His world is reducing despite all efforts to keep it interesting and busy. If we are at home, he walks upstairs at least twenty times in an hour and always tries the outside door as he passes it. Gates are now in place to keep him safe in the garden.

Sometimes it's as if I am superfluous and I can feel lonely and burdened. Caring can seem like a duty. When I am frustrated that Mike won't take off his pants or let me put his pyjamas on, or he leaves lights on, puts things in a safe place that no-one can locate, or can't find the bathroom when he needs it, I sometimes wonder whether I do enough to help him. At these times I leave the room to recover my equilibrium and try again. I am unsure what effect this anxiety has on my health. I sleep very poorly as Mike needs the loo every three or four hours. We still eat healthily, especially at this time of year when our home produce is plentiful. I have employed a cleaner to give me more time. However, I still rarely relax.

The deterioration in Mike's condition has become quite marked in the past few months. This means that I commit to fewer invitations until days before they are to take place. We no longer sleep away from home and have fewer guests to stay to keep our home as normal as possible for him. I love a party and, with help, we will again hold a garden party to thank everyone for their help and continued concern. We are fortunate to be so well supported! It must be terribly difficult without support especially with local authority cuts to social care."

The voices of Mike and Maureen's grandchildren

Ben: "It's difficult that we can't have a fun relationship with Pa now. He is not the same guy. I know it's the dementia but he is still a good Pa and we have some sound memories from our childhood."

Max: "I remember when Pa would have fallen down the cinema steps had I not reacted, grabbed him and stopped him from falling. At the time, I felt brave for catching him."

Tom: (about the football match) "I understood that Pa could not tell which goal to aim for because he has dementia and forgets things like rules. I wasn't angry, but I was disappointed because I wanted the boys to win."

Emma: "I was pleased the girls won and wasn't too upset at all."

Tom: "I understand that dementia is an illness that makes people forget things like how to drive, make meals and that it won't get better. It feels strange that Pa can't remember my name but I know he can't help it because of dementia."

Emma: "I don't worry about Pa not knowing my name: he knows me though, and that's fine."

Comments from Max, Tom and Emma's mother

Sharon: "Max does worry that he doesn't have a relationship anymore with Pa. His Pa doesn't seem to know him. He was very fond of his Grandpa and had lots of fun and attention when he was little and misses that interaction now with this distant man who barely acknowledges him."

Joan's story: looking back, looking forward

"After my father-in-law died, my mother-in-law Joan used to drive to visit us every Sunday, meeting us at church for Mass and then coming back with us for lunch. She loved to be involved in our choir but did not neglect her own parish. She went there to Mass followed by the Rosary every morning during the week and had some very long-standing friends.

Joan always brought an apple crumble for Sunday lunch and busied herself in the kitchen with the grandchildren. She prided herself on being practical, useful, on doing things for people. Gradually her mobility became more of a problem and although she still drove, she could not climb the stairs to the choir loft to join the choir or stand too long in the kitchen. I think she felt that her car was one of her lifelines since she needed it to get to her own church and to visit us. However, there is no doubt that her driving became very erratic – we used to drive behind her on the way home to lunch and I was reluctant to let the children go in her car.

Looking back, there were lots of little things that showed that all was not well. She had several little accidents or incidents in the car: she might not know where she was, bump another vehicle in the supermarket car park or stop suddenly and without warning.

Joan became very slow in the kitchen as if she was not quite sure what to do next. Sometimes she looked as if she was not sure whether she had just arrived or should be getting ready to go. So, we simply settled her into the sitting room every Sunday while we prepared lunch. Of course, that was difficult because she was very used to getting on with things and she did not like sitting when others were working. We encouraged the children to play cards with her but that did not last long because she became frustrated when she could not keep up with the game.

Joan used to be a home economics teacher and was brilliant at mending, making things do – and she loved ironing. I saved up easy mending for her and, whereas in the past she routinely brought her sewing kit with her, now she would have nothing to do with mending. Again looking back, I realise that she was not only having difficulty with her sight, which she would not admit, but also she had forgotten what to do. She still wanted to do the ironing, but I was quite nervous in case she might burn herself and, in the end, I persuaded her that standing for a length of time would not be good for her.

It was beginning to get quite difficult. Joan was feeling frustrated and sometimes angry, I think because she did not want us to think she was no longer useful or was a burden."

"Some of Joan's difficulties could be grouped under two headings: driving and family."

1 Driving

"Joan's failing health took place over quite a long time and the evidence sort-of built up. But I would like to have known at what point should we have done something about her driving. It was obvious that she was not going to give up voluntarily and I am not convinced that she told her GP everything.

I think the point when I did not want the children going in her car should have been the end of her driving but was difficult to have the conversation. We tried telling her that it would be less tiring if she took taxis, which she saw as a waste of money. I think it was her GP who eventually told her to stop driving, but that was after a series of mini-strokes.

I think that driving for Joan was a sign of her independence that she did not want to relinquish. She was also afraid that she would no longer be able to visit us on Sundays."

2 Family

We knew that Joan loved to visit us and especially enjoyed time with the grandchildren. Her own community had also been important. We also were aware that, once she could no longer drive, she did not visit her other adult children as often as previously.

"We can only work with what we know at the time. At the time we did not know that Joan had vascular dementia. At the same time, we were all reluctant to have any in-depth conversation with her about how she felt things were going because we did not want to upset her.

After Joan had given up the car, her daughter Sue used to collect her and bring her to church and our house as usual for Sundays. Sue began to realise that Joan's condition was more serious than we thought. She discovered that Joan was getting up hours before she needed to do so because it was taking her such a long time to get ready. Everything in her little house had a strict place and if she could not find something it was always because, in Joan's mind, someone else had moved it. Looking back, I think that these were some of the strategies that Joan had put in place for herself to manage what was happening.

Joan refused offers from parishioners at her church to get her to Mass or the Rosary, and after a while people stopped offering. She seemed to become more and more reliant on coming to us on Sundays and even said that that was the only thing to which she looked forward. I was concerned because this seemed to freeze out her other adult children. Joan's conversations with us around the lunch table became briefer and more of 'yes' 'no' answers rather than a proper chat.

Sue discovered from neighbours that Joan had been wandering outdoors at night. Joan had had a voice alarm fitted in case she needed help but she rang Sue one day in a panic saying that there was a man in the house – she could hear a man talking; later she thought the wall was talking.

Sue bought some videos of films that Joan had always liked. One day she found Joan afraid and panicking in front of the television, shouting at the actress on screen, telling her not to go out because she knew it would be dangerous.

As Joan was losing weight, Sue thought that Joan was not using the frozen meals which she had supplied. She was especially concerned that Joan was becoming very confused over her medication, taking wrong doses or forgetting altogether.

I think we all needed to be better informed about dementia. Perhaps this would have helped us to recognise some of the signs and to appreciate Joan's frustration."

Practical questions

- How do you talk to people about important things like driving, without looking as if you are taking away their independence or resorting to methods like hiding car keys, that might be seen as undermining them?
- How do you manage "strong characters" who do not admit to anyone that they are having problems?
- How can you help someone continue to feel useful?
- How do you recognise and adapt to someone's declining abilities without causing them distress and contributing to their sense of vulnerability and failure?
- How can you keep someone connected to their own community while also keeping up family routines?
- At what point should you look for professional help?

In hindsight

- What advice did you need?
- What advice would you give yourself?
- What did you need to help you and your family manage challenging situations?
- What did the person with dementia need?

Practical tips

- Rather than focusing on activities, spend more time quietly together so that there is the opportunity for a conversation.
- Make sure that you have good conversations with grandchildren since they may be very aware that things are not right and may feel to blame if Granny becomes frustrated or cross.

- Have a conversation with all members of the family about how things are going, how they would like to help and what people are prepared to do. Just keep talking to each other!
- Familiarise yourself with "quirkiness" which might indicate a need for more help.
- Simplify conversations: make them short, concrete and perhaps need only a yes/no answer.
- Remember that dementia can also take a toll on carers and families.
- Forgive yourself!
- Read up about the diagnosis and its effects and finding out information.
- Be prepared to seek professional help.

Rhoda and Malcolm's story

Rhoda talks about some of the practicalities of visiting her father Malcolm.

"I visit my father, who has dementia with Lewy bodies, as well as Parkinson's disease. Since December 2020 he has been in a care home. I visit him about once a week and speak to him on the phone briefly most days. I take him for appointments, deal with his affairs and have Power of Attorney for him. My brothers live further away so most of this responsibility falls on me.

It has been a case of learning from the time my father started to show symptoms of dementia a few years ago. This was also linked to the Parkinson's disease – for instance, the Parkinson's medication gave him hallucinations, but these also come with the dementia with Lewy bodies and have increased over time.

At first, he was living alone in the family home. One of the first crises happened because he was forgetting to take his medication correctly despite having an alarm, so I arranged for district nurses to visit four times a day.

We worked together to find my father a flat in an assisted living scheme. As it was also nearer to me, I could support him and the carers. After seventeen months there and following a fall resulting in a fractured hip, it was clear he needed more care, so we found a place for him in a care home.

The disease progresses and things change at each stage so you must constantly adjust what you do and how you interact with the person."

As with many of the people who talked to us, learning about dementia and how to cope seems to be hit-and-miss. Although Rhoda had some experience of dementia because her mother had Alzheimer's for several years before her death, Rhoda says,

"I have learned mostly from looking for information online and listening to the professionals he meets for his appointments (consultant, Parkinson's nurse, memory nurse, the psychiatrist at the memory clinic). However, at times I felt they didn't give me all the information I would have liked to receive. It is also good to talk to friends and family as they have anecdotes from their own experiences, but each person is different."

Rhoda also points to a common difficulty: that people are trying to juggle jobs and other things as well as caring.

"I would say I have often felt quite alone, but maybe I could have done more to connect with other people in my position of caring for/supporting a person with dementia. It was difficult to take the time out of a busy working life to go to groups at the time I may have needed it most, as I was already taking time out to support my dad when he was living on his own. The most supportive people were the Elderly Medicine Consultant and (briefly) the Memory Nurse over the phone. It would have been good to continue to receive support from the Memory Nurse as she understood the emotional effect on me as a carer and support person for my dad, but the team were overstretched and needed to help those in more dire circumstances, I think."

Voices from the Caritas Leeds Dementia Group and the people they have accompanied

Diagnosis

Dave's story

Dave was a secondary school teacher and a keen sportsman. Out of the blue he told his partner Sharon that he had decided to take early retirement, saying that he had no further interest in teaching. Financially, this did not create much of a strain and Sharon carried on with her own part-time job at the local primary school.

After a while Sharon noticed that Dave was doing little at home. He did not seem to engage with anything, took ages to get up and seemed reluctant to go out. If she asked him what he had done during the day, he became quite defensive. He seemed to spend most of the time in front of the television watching sport, and often – repeatedly – the same game.

When Sharon noticed that Dave was beginning to struggle with everyday conversations and could not seem to cope with simple tasks like buying the basic shopping, she persuaded him to visit the GP for a general check-up. Luckily, Dave did not mind Sharon coming to see the doctor with him. Together, they made a short list of things they should say. Dave admitted that he had found difficulties in working at the school, which is why he had wanted to retire. Dave eventually seemed quite relieved to visit the GP, who then arranged some tests.

Pete's experience
Pete felt numb when he received his diagnosis and it was only after some time had passed that he discovered questions which needed answers. He was conscious of the fact that the doctor spoke to the person with him rather than to himself. Pete was very concerned about the implications of his diagnosis and wanted help to come to terms with what this meant to him as well as an introduction to additional support services.

Planning services

Some people find that self-help books really help them to better manage their dementia. Others might need a booklet which explains dementia in non-medical terms. Planning should be tailored, as far as possible, to the needs of the individual.

Some examples

1 One lady was very open about her dementia and this disguised her vulnerability. She recalled how, on one occasion, a shopkeeper tried to take too much money from her. This led to an honest and insightful conversation in her support group with others who had experienced similar situations.

2 Another lady was willing to talk about her dementia and very articulate but would tire easily and needed consideration of what time of day activities would be held. Initially she could attend local groups alone as they were in a familiar location, but when the venue changed, she then needed help to get there. Access to community support in reaching social activities is invaluable.

3 A younger person found the dementia café difficult as it was full of much older people than himself. He found a patient support group at his doctor's surgery much more helpful as he met people with varied abilities and made new friends.

4 Someone who attended her local dementia café was upset when sitting next to carers who wanted to speak amongst themselves. They had not intended this, but it made her feel excluded.

People living with dementia:

- often need opportunities to involve people directly in the planning of their dementia-friendly services. This can boost their sense of self and ensure their needs are taken seriously.
- sometimes want to take part in research and have their voices heard. It is important for them to be given a choice.
- want access to tools and resources which can provide the tools they need to help themselves.

- want an opportunity to define their condition and abilities for themselves in a positive way which affirms their life experience.
- in the early stages of dementia, value peer support. They don't just want services to be done for them, they want to support themselves and to be made to feel they have something to offer.
- are helped by seating plans which place them with people of similar needs or at similar stages of their journey, with common interests.
- want you to remember that they are people. Like people everywhere, they are unique, varied and come in all shapes and sizes. We are all created in God's image.

An experience of accompaniment: Margaret's story

"My experience of being part of the Alzheimer's Society Side-by-Side project is to experience the possibility of living well despite dementia.

The project enables someone with dementia to do things they enjoy and which they can no longer do alone. Each person is matched with a volunteer who has similar interests. I have heard of pairs attending boxing matches, playing golf, visiting museums and art galleries, seeing garden centres, wandering around the shops, walking the dog and having a good chat over a cup of tea and piece of cake. Most people would not engage in all the above!

I was matched with a man whom we will call John, who knew the local area very well, whereas I was a recent arrival. He enjoyed sharing his great knowledge through walks in the town and visiting the museums and art galleries or garden centres, always including a cup of coffee and cake, preferably chocolate cake for him, or a scone.

We were blessed in that John's wife, Annie, prompted him to tell me the things he needed me to be aware of when we were out. We should board the bus at the bus station to be sure of seats, even if this meant a longer walk. Stairs or, better still, lifts, were the best way to change floors. When walking on rough pavements or crossing roads John would like support as his balance and vision were not as good as previously. This reminded me that dementia affects more than the memory. We agreed that John would either take my arm or hand when he felt the need. He was highly amused that people who knew him and saw us together would be speculating on the woman with whom he was holding hands, knowing it was not his wife! To his delight we did meet such friends of his on our travels. John was also keen that I should note the whereabouts of toilets. I developed a way of loitering near, but not too near, the gents!

As we moved along the queue at the café, John's natural chivalry demanded that he carry the tray and his dementia made this unwise. Finding ways to maintain his dignity while ensuring his safety sometimes required creative thinking! Allowing John to open the butter wrapper in his own way when his dexterity was reduced required patience while allowing him to do what he could, rather than de-skill him by doing it for him. Reduced dexterity can be another sign of the dementia affecting different parts of the brain and its impact on different functions or skills.

I learnt the topics that John liked to talk about. If he seemed to be getting a little upset or confused, I would introduce familiar topics. For instance, I had heard he had flown on Concorde and been in the RAF. John had also taken a wing walk, raising £3000 for the Alzheimer's Society and this was also a favourite topic. On landing, he wanted to go back up again as he enjoyed it so much. Annie, waiting anxiously on the ground was not so enamoured, although her pride in John was clear and justifiable.

John was in his early seventies when we met. Another person with whom I was paired would sometimes ask to stay at home and play Scrabble. Her word power was excellent, although I was deputed to total the scores.

While the aim of Side-by-Side is to support the person living with dementia, the fact that they are enjoying an outing can offer the spouse/carer a little respite to rest or visit family, etc.

Dementia is not a natural part of aging and can be diagnosed in much younger people. Someone in their twenties or thirties can find it difficult to access dementia awareness groups with their peers.

I found that the training I received was a great help in accompanying someone with dementia. One piece of advice, for example, was to follow their lead, staying in their reality as much as possible.

Asked by a ninety-year-old when her mum was coming home, I invited her to tell me about her mum. Pointing out that her mother had died would not have been helpful and would have caused sadness. Looking for her mum possibly indicated that she was feeling a bit insecure. The conversation about her mother offered the elderly lady the chance to feel her mum's love in her absence.

Before going out with a new person I always try to build up some knowledge of their likes and dislikes and calming topics. It does not matter how often someone tells the story or asks the same question, it is new to them and deserves compassion from the listener, who should ideally respond as if hearing it for the first time.

The language we use can help to raise awareness and reduce the stigma of dementia. 'Person living with dementia' rather than 'dementia sufferer' is more appropriate because, although it is true this disease can and does cause suffering, we need to be aware of the person first and their condition second. It is not only the person who is diagnosed who is living with the dementia."

A Sister of Mercy thinks about caring for Sisters with dementia in a religious community

"The most important thing for me to remember is that these people are my sisters; frail perhaps, vulnerable, exasperating on occasion, but still my sisters.

The pace in community becomes much slower: meals are not rushed; no one must dash off for meetings or appointments in the same way. Presence becomes much more central; there is much for me to learn.

Our foundress Catherine McAuley said to 'keep patience ever at your side, you'll need it for a constant guide'. These are wise words with which I live with varying degrees of success.

Fidelity to a gentle structure is very important for Sisters who have dementia. It helps to have set times for prayers, meals and times for relaxing together, as Sisters need the security of the presence of others, particularly if they have lived largely in institutional settings. Spending time with them each day is vital to really get to know them, find connections with them to listen and tune in emotionally to their fears and joys. For some, this may mean playing cards. For others, reading poetry or singing old folk songs from childhood or doing the crossword together might be a very positive moment.

Accompaniment of Sisters like this can be draining, so it's very important to care for yourself in order to be able to be really present when with them."

Peggy, a dementia friend training in action

"My training and experiences of people living with dementia has taught and shown me never to underestimate what they can do, instead of stressing what they cannot do.

One example of this was a person living with dementia in a community environment, who did not speak and appeared to be unaware of what was happening around her. I facilitated the community in a in a simple PE exercise with appropriate music as I demonstrated the exercises. I sat in front of this person and held her hands and smiled. She followed my expression and seemed to enjoy all that was happening and, to our amazement, suddenly shouted in a very audible voice, 'You are all a lot of fools'. The unexpected remark caused us all to laugh – including the speaker! Her mood had changed for the rest of the day.

Someone living with dementia senses the atmosphere of their surroundings in a way which is vital for their ongoing wellbeing.

In visiting a centre for people living with dementia, I watched as a staff member distributed cups of tea to the group. One resident sipped her drink and then shouted, screamed and spat it out – earning herself a reprimand which might have affected her mood for the rest of the day. My training had taught me that all difficult or aggressive behaviour is someone's way of trying to communicate something is not right. Perhaps this person liked sugar in her tea and there was none, or it had sugar and she did not like it this way. It may have been too cold and she liked it hot. Although it would have taken extra time, what a difference it would have made if only the member of staff had known how each liked their tea!

I had a very good friend living with dementia. She was Irish and a retired teacher who loved children and had taught them to dance. During my weekly visits, we clapped our hands and sang whilst watching a video of the children dancing in their costumes. Together, we saw it innumerable times but, for my friend, it was always the first occasion.

A cup of tea in the kitchen usually followed the video. One Sunday, as I went to switch off the television, my friend unexpectedly said my name and announced that I should 'be sure all the children have a glass of orange juice and a biscuit'. I was amazed and speechless as I experienced for myself the extent to which dementia can affect people's perception. To my friend, these children were truly present in the room.

This may not happen to everyone with dementia. Despite a common diagnosis, each experiences dementia differently.

Through my friend, I also realised that we need to be careful when sitting people with dementia alone in front of a television.

Communication is possible with people with dementia, but we must enter their agenda as many are not able to enter ours. It helps if we can learn something about their history. Appropriate music, touch, silence and simply being in their presence are all very powerful ways of communication. Wherever possible, pets and children are both therapeutic and great ways of communication for our loved ones with dementia.

I visited a friend with whom I had worked for many years in my teaching career. She was in the later stages of dementia and I was not sure if she would recognise me. I had brought some photographs but she did not respond at first – until I showed her one of myself. Her face lit up and she pointed to me and smiled. She had made the connection. I was so pleased.

Music has a language of its own.

One friend whom I visited was very distressed. I put on some relaxing music, sat in front of her and stroked her hands. She calmed down slowly but when she heard some familiar songs, she began to sing them with me and, by the time I left, her mood seemed very much improved.

On another occasion, when a lady in a wheelchair and I danced slowly to background music, she laughed with delight.

Silence is also a very powerful communicator. It can make a difference just to be present to someone by sitting with them.

At first, I was unsure how to cope when I found someone very distressed. I would leave them alone – but then I discovered that some personal attention worked amazingly well. It was also an important opportunity to glimpse the person beyond their diagnosis. They still needed to be noticed – and it was so important to them.

Patients react to pets in their company and talk to them with great affection. To see a dog wag its tail in delight in their company is itself delightful.

On one occasion, a lively two-year-old child delighted the residents in a care home as she went from one to the other with great hugs and laughter. One lady, who did not respond much to anyone, engaged with the child in chuckles and great delight.

In difficult situations, it is worth trying something you think may work. If it doesn't, then don't worry: try something else. If you are communicating and helping to bring joy and value to the person's life, that is all that matters.

People with dementia are still unique people and deserve our support understanding and respect. People need to know what is happening to them. For instance, I saw two care home staff members lift a terrified, screaming resident from a chair to a hoist without communicating with her before or during their actions. Explanations matter and can make the difference between compliance and non-compliance, calmness and sheer terror."

Reflection from the Leeds Dementia Group on the effects of the covid pandemic

The covid lockdown caused many delays in:

- post-diagnostic support by a memory nurse;
- diagnosis because of closed memory clinics;
- receiving prescribed medication to possibly delay the onset of dementia symptoms.

Some important losses included:

- loss of enjoyment and support gained through meeting others in similar situations;
- the closure of day support centres;
- loss of shared, face-to-face activities such as memory cafés and singing groups;
- loss or changes of familiar routines and structures;
- inability to attend religious services in person or to receive Holy Communion from a Eucharistic Minister;
- reduced access to the sacraments;
- interrupted regular contact with family, friends and community members;
- lost opportunities for activities such as shopping;
- death of one or more family members because of covid infection.

Reflecting

As a result of these losses, many people experienced low mood and depression, perhaps increased because not everyone understood the need to wear a face mask or for social distancing. Dementia is a hidden disability and so people could find themselves judged for their non-compliance with masks or for not maintaining social distances.

People with dementia cope best when they have a routine which offer structure and familiarity, but the restrictions imposed by the pandemic caused major changes in these routines. The ritual of prayer and the opportunity to attend faith services either online or on TV helped to sustain people's religious beliefs and kept them in regular contact with their faith community.

Many people experienced increased social isolation as the day support activities that were available closed due to the pandemic. Whilst some people adapted well to these restrictions with the offer of community support with shopping and telephone support, others felt increasingly frustrated by the lack of face-to-face support.

Memory cafés and singing groups are very popular and some moved online but moving back to face-to-face support and activities can still create difficulties.

The Leeds Dementia Group found that caring for someone with dementia can be emotional and demanding but, above all, tremendously rewarding. This was particularly true through the pandemic when it was a privilege to be able to support people through the crisis. One resident told us that she felt very safe in our care.

Losing a resident during this time was challenging but also an honour to be with them in their final days when family were unable to do so. With faith, love, support and hope of those around us, we look forward to better days ahead.

Covid: a personal story – what the pandemic meant for Anne

"During the pandemic, when so many people suffered loss, hardship and distress, I was one of the fortunate ones. However, what was hard for me was being parted for so long from my dearly loved husband. Malcolm suffers from severe Alzheimer's disease and has been cared for by the Mercy Care Centre in Beaumont House since September 2018.

The home went into lockdown on 17 March 2020 and we were unable to see our loved ones at all for three months. However, from the start, the Mercy Care Centre made it a priority to facilitate contact and communication between residents and their family and friends. The home immediately set up a Facebook page where we could keep up to date on what was going on in the home, post photographs, videos and messages and keep in touch with each other. We also set up a relatives' WhatsApp group and, when we could, we met up for coffee and a chat in Darley Park and even managed a lunch together.

When lockdown eased during summer months, the home erected a gazebo and marquees with garden furniture so that we could enjoy the garden visits and, latterly, a comfortable purpose-built visiting room has been constructed.

I was overwhelmed with joy when, once again in June, I was able to see Malcolm and enjoy special times together during the summer. The second lockdown was a blow but the home ensured that we managed to continue with window visits.

Throughout the pandemic, despite my sorrow at not being part of Malcolm's life for a year, I was comforted by knowing that the wonderful staff at the Mercy Care Centre looked after him with their constant compassion, care and loving kindness. Now dear Malcolm is approaching the end of his life and I can be with him at last. I am so grateful that we can be together for this final part of the journey."

A last word

As a dementia develops, the person's relationship with God continues in ways we cannot know. The person with a dementia may reach a time when they are living fully in the present moment. What gifts can we learn from people at this stage of life?

Our role is to support the evolving relationship with God for a person living with dementia, just as we aim to do for anyone else. Our society values function, efficiency, speed and usefulness. Through conditions like dementia, we are beginning to understand that living life well is not simply about function and usefulness.

We all need to start thinking here and now about simply being with people, enjoying the company of others, enjoying the world outside. Above all we need to question ourselves: do we judge people by what they can do for us? If this is the case, we may fear that that is also how we are being judged.

Reflections for the reader:

- Do you have a story to share?
- Have you been able to share your story in the past?
- What strategies might help in sharing your story with others?

Chapter 2

Talking about what matters to you

People live in relationships. Dementia-friendly communities must therefore take account of the needs and wants of the individual, both on their own and in their relationship with others. These include both:

- the person living with dementia
- families and carers.

In our first two chapter, we identified five groups of people, each with its specific needs:

- people living with dementia
- families and carers
- people who accompany them
- clergy and Religious.

Effective action

This is a three-stage process:

- **listen** to people with dementia, their families, carers and those who accompany them
- **ask** people about what matters to them
- **tailor** actions and resources to expressed, actual needs and wants.

We listened to people, asked about what they considered important and then reflected upon their words and expressed needs.

What we learnt

The individual, their family and carers have important needs:

- to find out and to know the potential diagnosis
- to **hear** the diagnosis
- to manage after the diagnosis
- to cope with change
- for tailor-made support in identifying the next steps
- for good communication
- to talk about what matters.

Need to find out and to know the potential diagnosis

Dave's story shows that often the very early stages of dementia are simply not apparent, especially when a person lives with someone who assumes the responsibility for daily activities such as shopping, cooking and cleaning. Moreover, people, especially long-established couples, are accustomed to each other's ways.

Sometimes family members, notably grown-up children, first notice changes in someone's behaviour and begin to think that things are not right. They may not initially suspect that these changes are due to dementia and may not want to be seen as interfering. Nevertheless, encouraging the person to visit their GP for a general check-up may be a good way forward because this ensures that all concerns and worries can be considered.

It is important that the GP sees the individual in person regarding their health and well-being, and involves them from the outset in any decisions about treatment. Usefully, the doctor will probably recognise any changes in a long-standing patient.

As Maureen's story demonstrates, letting close family members, especially adult children, know about tests and a diagnosis, can help the family grow used to the new reality of their loved one's life. However, family members should be aware that issues of consent and confidentiality come into play. In the chapter on ethics, we will see that a healthcare professional may be unable to discuss a patient's diagnosis, care and treatment with other people, even close family members, without the patient's consent.

Maggie's story shows how difficult it is for friends or parishioners who want to help but are concerned not to intrude into another person's privacy.

Visiting the GP

Everyone forgets things at times and as people grow older, they may find daily activities more and more of a challenge. This does not mean that they have dementia.

Dementia can be difficult to diagnose. The GP will also want to rule out other problems, for instance confusion can be due to an infection or perhaps a lack of engagement due to depression or anxiety.

Although there is no one test for dementia a, GP can get some idea of how things are with a person by taking a personal history and assessing everyday coping capabilities. This is where Dave found it useful to have Sue go with him to his appointment.

The NHS recommends that someone who knows the person well accompanies them so that they can:

- describe noticed changes or problems
- remember what has been said.

The GP will make an overall assessment by checking:

- prescribed medication
- self-prescribed items such as vitamins or herbal remedies
- pre-existing conditions such as high blood pressure, diabetes, depression, stroke or heart conditions
- short and long-term memory, attention span and concentration, communication and awareness skills through simple pen and paper cognition tests. The tests are not there to assess how clever a person is. It is useful to mention if there is anything that might affect these tests, for instance the person may have dyslexia or English may not be their first language, a point which is not always obvious to a healthcare professional.

The GP may:

- make a referral to a specialist

- arrange for blood tests and scans. It is important to let the doctor know if you have any worries about these tests.

Need for the diagnosis

Waiting for and then receiving a diagnosis can be a difficult and troubling time for anyone. Whatever our worries, a final diagnosis may come as a shock or, for some people, it will be a relief because it explains what they have already suspected.

A diagnosis starts the process of finding the right treatment and support so that the person with dementia can continue to live an active and fulfilling life, and prepare for the future.

Many people who receive a difficult diagnosis, whether it be for dementia, cancer or any potentially life-changing condition, have a similar reaction: it is hard to take in the news and even harder to ask the right questions.

In some of our conversations it was clear that the person with dementia:

- found the diagnosis overwhelming and forgot to ask questions
- felt overlooked and excluded from the conversation between the doctor and the person's companion
- felt disempowered and already dependent on others because the dialogue was about them but did not include them.

Need to manage after the diagnosis

Many of the people to whom we spoke said that they were really interested in managing their own conditions, or helping their loved one, and they wanted to find out more. People want to have access to tools and resources. However, as one man put it, they often want explanations that are presented in non-medical terms. Moreover, they want to have an opportunity to understand dementia in a positive way which affirms their life experience. Additionally, it is important for people to realise that they are not alone in this journey.

Sharing stories can be a significant way of mutual support and it can also be a way of sharing good practice and helpful strategies. As a dementia friend explained, the people to whom she spoke wanted to offer something themselves as peer support. This has tremendous value because it shows that people with dementia do have something to contribute.

Many find that getting together gives them the opportunity to talk about difficult situations in which they have found themselves, to compare their experience and to be supported by people who have encountered similar situations. Meeting people who know what the journey is like is helpful for everyone, whether they are people living with dementia, their families and carers, or those who accompany them.

Need to cope with change: learning from the effects of covid

The covid pandemic changed many things for everyone, affecting the usual avenues of support and care. As one person pointed out, the loss of face-to-face activities and support during the pandemic was hard. As we come out of the pandemic, we have all learned some important lessons.

For some people the prospect of going out and mixing with other people seems daunting. Some people are worried that they will be judged or that they will let themselves down. There may be a great temptation just to hide away. Some people lose the incentive to go out and meet people. Others experience low mood and depression, making it even harder to leave the house. For many people the complications of simply getting ready and making choices about the right clothes for the day becomes too much. People's experiences during Covid lockdowns showed us that social isolation leads to loneliness and additional strains on family carers, sometimes with the risk of frustrations boiling over. Face-to-face activities, simple outings with other people, or even having a cup of coffee with other people, can help people to keep connected and slowly to adapt to changes. It also helps to set up a good routine. Research has shown that people with dementia cope best when they have a routine which offers structure and familiarity.

As dementia friends have said, dementia is a hidden disability so please do not judge.

Need for tailor-made support in identifying the next steps

Memory cafes and singing groups are very popular and some were delivered online during the Covid pandemic. Face-to-face support has its own challenges.

- Timing - people often tire easily.
- Location – it helps if groups are local or in familiar settings.
- Community support – to help people attend social activities.
- Group dynamics

- Attention must be given to the people who come to the groups so that, for instance, younger people with dementia can find support that is age-appropriate for them.
- Careful consideration of seating plans to place people with dementia together with people of similar needs or at similar stages of their journey, with common interests and abilities, might help to avoid any sense of exclusion or isolation.

As one of our dementia friends says, the really important point is that people with dementia are people and so, like everybody else, they are unique, varied and come in all shapes and sizes, with different interests, likes and dislikes. Moreover, working with people living with dementia brings with it some real surprises. Penny says that she has learned never to underestimate what people can do and has found many moments of unexpected smiles, laughter and words. As she explains, a person living with dementia can pick up the atmosphere around her and it is important to realise this to help people live well. Laughter is, after all, contagious.

Working with people with dementia also brings with it insights, especially when it comes to perceived "difficult" behaviour. Often aggressive behaviour stems from frustration or the need to communicate that something is not right.

Taking the time to know a person, especially finding out about their likes and dislikes, from how they take their cup of tea to whether they feel the cold, can make all the difference, and sometimes that difference lasts for the rest of the day. Dementia may ask us all to alter our own perceptions.

People with dementia often live in the present and they may interpret reality in a different way that is nevertheless meaningful to them. A common experience is that videos, films or television are lived as if it is the present moment. As Joan's story shows, that can be frightening for people who think something on screen is actually happening here and now.

Need for good communication

Good communication is necessary for everyday interaction with people. But it also incorporates human dignity, understanding, respect and the regard we have for others.

The failure to tell a person what is going to happen and why can create real fear in someone who does not understand or know what is going on.

Good communication is vital to making connections and forming relationships. It happens in very many ways, through speech, through gestures and actions, and simply just by being with someone.

Poor communication frequently causes concerns if we overlook its variability and use one means only.

As dementia takes hold, people often experience increasing difficulty in finding the words needed to express their thoughts. It may be up to family and carers to initiate conversation.

Helpful hints

- Speak clearly, slowly and in short sentences.
- Keep eye contact.

- Wait for a response.
- Rephrase questions so that they are easier to answer.
- Enter their agenda as many people are not able to enter ours, by learning:
  - ◊ something about their story
  - ◊ the music they like
  - ◊ the hobbies they enjoy.
- Try different strategies.
- Check with relatives or someone who knows the person well to ensure the person is not, for example, frightened of animals.
- Have realistic expectations when it comes to finding points of contact.
- Be prepared to spend time with someone.
- Give personal attention through your willingness to be present.

Discovering something that works can make everybody happy!

Talk about what matters: a tool

Thinking through these stories gave us the building blocks to see how we could work better with people to address their needs and wants. From this process, we developed a tool that may be useful in different situations and in creating dementia-friendly parishes, communities and dioceses.

The aim is to make the most of conversations that people are probably already having, but to do so with an eye to using the information gained in a practical way. Rather than formulate specific questions or surveys, the tool suggests some prompt questions for the person leading the conversation. This seems to be a more natural and user-friendly approach. It also allows people to tell their own stories, and having someone listen to your story is, we found, a basic need. The important thing to note is that this toolkit is not like a set questionnaire, nor is it the only way to go about hearing what people must say. As our chapter on dementia voices shows, people have different kinds of conversations, in different places and at different times. We hope this toolkit may be useful as a way of remembering what people say.

The prompt questions for each group are framed in terms of what enables people and what are the barriers, based on:

- the burning issues for people living with dementia
- the needs, wants and wishes of the person with dementia
- the needs, wants and wishes of families and carers
- useful help or resources for accompaniers
- useful resources for clergy and religious.

In conducting the interview:

- prepare the interviewee in advance of conducting it
- provide a relaxed, comfortable and secure setting
- consider going through the questions before asking them
- ensure the interviewee understands the questions
- adapt to circumstances
- be prepared to terminate the interview according to the needs of the interviewee
- be sensitive to verbal and non-verbal signs
- welcome advocates (family members or carers) who can help people speak up for themselves and whose viewpoint might be valuable.

In using the information from the interview:

- consider its ethical use
- show respect for the individual
- obtain consent
- involve relatives and significant others so that they:
    - ◊ are aware of the conversation
    - ◊ can help where necessary.

A general chat beforehand as part of the conversation can help to break the ice and check how the person is feeling. If the person is not feeling so good, then it may be an indication that they are not up to carrying on the conversation.

Information sheet

My name is .... and I am a member of [e.g. the Caritas Leeds Dementia Group]

[If you are doing this in person perhaps add a photograph.]

We would like to have a conversation with you to find out what matters to you, what works for you and what does not work for you. We want to find out how you feel you are being supported and what support you think you would like. We would like you to tell us how your church community could help you.

The information you give us will be kept confidential and will be anonymous. It will not affect the service you are currently receiving. We will use it in a book to help inform people accompanying people with dementia and to help develop dementia-friendly parishes.

If at any stage you do not want to participate any further, please just say. If you want a break but would like to talk to us again, please tell us.

Here are my contact details:................

Thank you.

Conversation with the person living with dementia

These prompt questions must be adapted to the individual. Consider whether the interviewee would prefer:

- picture cues (some might find this patronising)
- to give detailed answers
- yes/no answers.

Think about:

- what the person wished they had had
- what the person needs and wants now
- what would enable this
- barriers to achieving wishes, needs and wants
- possible practical outcomes.

You may like to ask:

- How are you feeling?
- Do you feel happy?
- How are things working for you?

If the person indicates that they want to talk about their story and their diagnosis then you might ask:

- Can you tell me what happened when you first were diagnosed with dementia? *This question can prompt you to choose to ask some of the questions below, e.g.:*
- Did you think something was wrong?
- Did anyone go with you to the doctor?
- Did you get all the information you needed?
- Were you offered any help?
- How confident do you feel now?

- Do you feel confident going out on your own?
    - ◊ Would you like to go out more?
    - ◊ What would help you go out more?
- What do you like doing?
    - ◊ What stops you from doing what you like?
    - ◊ What would help you do more?
- Is there anything you miss?
    - ◊ What is stopping you do these things?
    - ◊ What would help you do these things again?
- Who matters to you?
- How do you think your family/wife/children are?
    - ◊ Do you worry about them?
    - ◊ What could help them?
- Do you go to church?
    - ◊ How does that work out for you?
    - ◊ Would you like someone to talk about your spiritual life?
- Do you worry about the future? *This may raise questions about the immediate future, the possibility of a move to a care home or questions about dying – be prepared!*

Be aware that some people may be adamant that they do not have dementia.

Conversation with families and carers

Sometimes families and carers just want to talk, and this might direct your conversation. You may like to ask:

- Do you feel supported?
- Who do you rely on for your own support?

- How important is it for you to talk to people who share your experience of dementia?
- Can you say what you needed at different stages:
  - ◊ when your loved one was first diagnosed?
  - ◊ as the dementia progressed?
  - ◊ now?
  - ◊ thinking ahead?
- Do you feel supported by the Church?
  - ◊ What more should the Church do?
  - ◊ And your church community?

Conversation with people accompanying and with supporters

This section is about talking with people who accompany or support a person living with dementia. The first part (about important skills and attitudes) is designed to recognise that the supporter is already doing an important job and has their own insights from what they do – it is getting people to realise that, for example, listening is an important skill but also allowing the person to lead a conversation on how it is going so they can reflect on their own practice. The second question is finding out if they need training (but framed as "Do you think people need training?", then, more directly, "Do you need support?"

This may begin with asking how the interviewee came to accompany a person with dementia or their family, or how they came to be a supporter. You may want to ask:

- What skills and attitudes do you think are important for people accompanying a person living with dementia?
  - ◊ Listening and communication skills?

  - ◊ Any other skills?
  - ◊ Being informed about dementia and its different forms?
  - ◊ Ability to deal with challenging behaviour?
- Do you think people need training?
  - ◊ Where would this come from?
- Do you also need support?
  - ◊ Where would this come from?
- If you are involved in a church community, how can we improve what we do?
  - ◊ What would help you?
  - ◊ What does not help you?
- What resources do you need?

Conversation with clergy and Religious

- Do you see your parish or your community as dementia-friendly?
- How can your parish or community contact and maintain contact with people living with dementia and their families?
- What resources do you have in the parish or community?
- What about hidden resources that are as yet untapped?
- How can the diocese help you in your parish or community?
- What help is available from the Conference of Religious (CoR)?
- Do you join the webinars and workshops on dementia offered through the Conference of Religious?
- Do you need any support with access to, or provision of, the sacraments?
- Is dementia an area for your ongoing formation?

And what matters in the end?

In our conversations much was said about living well with dementia. However, one gap we have identified is spiritual care, and dying well with dementia. In Chapter 3 we reflect on some strategies for living well with dementia and then, in Chapter 4, we will explore dying well with dementia.

While we recognise that our identification of four distinct groups, (i) people living with dementia, (ii) families and carers, (iii) people who accompany them and (iv) clergy and religious, may be artificial, and we accept that there will be overlaps, we think it is helpful to address each of these groups when it comes to living and dying well.

Reflection for the reader:

How do you remember and record what matters to you?

Chapter 3

Living well with dementia: what works for you?

Living well with dementia and living with good care concerns everyone: people with dementia, their families and carers, those who accompany them and those people who support them spiritually.

Living well with dementia also means taking account of some of the more challenging realities. In naming some of these challenges we do not take away from living well. Rather, we hope that we can give strategies for coping, conscious that human beings are very creative in finding ways to live well.

In this chapter we explore strategies for living well and what might work to create dementia-friendly communities. However, since the person living with dementia is at the heart of any strategy, we begin by looking at how people are included in the conversation, their personal storytelling and their participation in decision-making.

Telling my story

In our previous chapters we have looked at the conversations we have had with people with dementia and their families, to identify possible needs and wants. We think that these complement other, pre-existing activities.

This is me

This is me is an important leaflet produced by the Alzheimer's Society and refined by feedback from people living with dementia, their families, carers and professionals.[1] It is designed for people who cannot easily share information about themselves when they are in unfamiliar places with unfamiliar people and has proved to be a valuable resource, enabling health and social care professionals to deliver care tailored to the person's needs.

This is me allows someone to:

- attach a favourite photo of themself
- give the name they like to be called
- say where they live
- identify the people who know them best
- include what they feel is important for other people to know:

[1] https://www.alzheimers.org.uk/sites/default/files/2020-03/this_is_me_1553.pdf

- ◊ basic information about hearing, eyesight and mobility
- ◊ preferred methods of communication
- ◊ cultural, religious and spiritual background
- ◊ routines, likes, dislikes and preferences
- ◊ "advanced plans"
- ◊ appointed attorney with decision-making powers on their behalf.

Life Story Work

The organisation Dementia UK has promoted an activity called Life Story Work.[2]

In this activity a person living with dementia is supported by family and professionals to gather information from past events and experiences to build up a personal biography. A personal biography is another way of telling someone's life story. It helps other people see what events have mattered to them, how they have coped in the past, what experiences have made them who they are. It can also help to express some of their values, hopes, wishes and desires.

Sharing a personal biography enables other people to share in someone's story and in this way everyone's relationships can be enriched, perhaps through the use of pictures, photographs, objects, DVDs and anything else which might help in enhancing their personal biographies.

Of course, not everyone wants to share their stories and some people will not want to look back on certain areas of their life.

[2] https://www.dementiauk.org/for-professionals/free-resources/life-story-work/

Those helping with this project must be sensitive to the other person's concerns and we hope that our conversation tool may help in this. Sometimes, reflecting on difficult times or on troubling memories can be painful and it is not appropriate to go down a route that will cause distress. The best way is to follow the lead of the individual who is giving their story and reassure them that they do not have to remember everything or share everything.

Nor should the project be rushed. Instead, there could be a focus on joy, which is often a combination of shades and light, spending time together, all the while remembering that life continues so that there will be more things to add.

Knowing what people like and dislike, what music they enjoy, whether they like the outdoors, or animals, television programmes, films, books or hobbies, whether they are "larks" or "owls", will help, not only in finding points of connection with other people or activities, but also in helping them live their life fully.

Good communication can help identify not just likes and dislikes, but also something more profound: their spiritual needs. Communicating what really matters in a personal biography can improve and inform decision-making at significant moments in people's lives, including the time when they are approaching the end of life.

Decision-making processes

We make decisions all the time, from routine events such as what time to get up, what to wear and eat and to plan activities, all the way to more important decisions such as where to live and what medical treatment we want to have.

In making even an apparently simple decision, we automatically take on board, understand and remember pieces of information and evaluate many different factors. Often, we seek advice from friends, family and experts. Think, for example, about deciding what to wear for the day: our choice may depend on what is in the wardrobe, on how we are feeling and what we are planning to do – and it makes sense to consult the weather forecast. I may make an unwise choice such as not taking a coat when it looks cold outside, but an unwise choice does not mean to say that I cannot make my own decisions.

Many elements influence decision-making and these include not just our choices and preferences but also our past experiences, emotions and stresses, appreciation of risks involved, economic situation and, significantly, our cultural and religious beliefs.

Each of the many different conditions that come under the general term dementia has its own progression and symptoms.

In early-stage dementia a person can usually manage everyday decisions and may need little help. For example, Denis was happy going to the local shops and used the ATM machine for cash. But on several occasions, he forgot to take his bank card and, sometimes, to collect his cash from the machine. He found it much easier and less embarrassing when he and his wife Janet made sure he had a set amount of money with him for his purchases.

As dementia progresses the person may have more difficulty in making decisions because dementia eventually affects the way in which somebody takes on board, processes, remembers and understands information before weighing up their choices.

Denis and Janet had always enjoyed a meal and a glass of wine in the pub with their friends. Janet noticed that when they were out, Denis began to drain his first glass in one go and would then pour himself a few more, seemingly forgetting how much he was drinking. Janet would gently remind him and suggest that he had a soft drink if he felt thirsty.

At this stage Janet had to decide whether Denis' decision to have more glasses of wine mattered enough to intervene, especially considering the risks involved.

In this example from Denis and Janet we can see some of the complications surrounding decision-making.

- Supporting the person living with dementia to make their own decisions means consciously thinking about what they would want and perhaps facilitating their choice.
- The possibilities of impaired decision-making can carry risks.
- A person can make an unwise or unusual decision and this does not mean that they do not have a capacity for decision-making.

Talking to Denis, Janet explained her concerns calmly and gently, gave the information he needed to make his choice, offered the option of a different drink and gave him time to think about what he wanted. Looking into the future, Janet decided that it would be better if she and Denis sometimes met their friends in a coffee shop instead of the pub. If they were out where alcohol was served, she would make sure the bottle was not within Denis' reach.

What do you think? Should Janet intervene and reduce the options for Denis?

Janet also had to think about what information she should give to others about Denis' condition. Their friends knew of his diagnosis of dementia, but as a matter of confidentiality, Janet did not think it appropriate to mention this to the bar staff. Denis was well-known at the local shops and after checking with him, they simply told the local shopkeepers that Denis could be a little forgetful at times. One shopkeeper was more than happy to "keep an eye out" for him and spent time chatting to Denis every time he came into the shop.

Decision-making and the Mental Capacity Act

In Chapter 5, *Making the legislation work for you,* Lucy Marie Antonia Cortis, a solicitor, describes in detail the Mental Capacity Act 2005, the ways in which people can prepare ahead of time and she explains some of the terms used in the legislation.

This next section explains in simpler terms the basics of capacity and decision-making.

In Denis and Janet's story, Denis could make decisions about going out with friends and about his choice of drink. As his dementia progressed, Denis became less able to judge how much he was drinking and Janet did her best to help Denis in his choice. When it became clearer that Denis needed more support, Janet altered what they did by suggesting an outing to a coffee shop rather than the pub. This was the least restrictive option.

Some decisions are easier than others, for example what to do or what to wear may be easier and have less serious consequences than whether to have a particular treatment or where to live. This should not prevent someone from making the decisions they can make, possibly with support in the process.

Keep in mind the essentials. Someone may:

- have the capacity to decide and should be allowed to do so
- be able to make some decisions but not others
- have a limited decision-making capacity, which could be enhanced with appropriate support
- be unable to make decisions despite support. Any choice which others make on their behalf must be in the person's best interests and must be the least restrictive.

When couples have lived together for a long time some decisions seem to come naturally: "My husband always makes me a cup of coffee in the morning: he never asks if I would prefer tea." There is a natural tendency to "think for" the other person, especially when it comes to daily activities and going places. But imagine the following scenario:

Jack and Jill have been married for many years and they live in the family home. Their grown-up children now live some distance away. Jack's dementia is now severe. Jill and the family think it is wise for them to move nearer their children so that they can be better supported. Jill knows that Jack loves seeing his children and grandchildren so there is no question in her mind that this is what Jack would want. She decides to sell the house and buy something more manageable near the family. But Jack and Jill jointly own the house and the solicitor has said that both must sign the legal papers for the sale. However, Jack no longer has legal capacity to sign the papers. What are their options?

Although the above case describes Jack's dementia as severe, mental capacity is not about someone's general competence.

Mental capacity concerns the ability to make a specific decision at a specific time. Given that Jack has severe dementia it is unlikely that he can make the decision to sell the house he owns with Jill. However, this lack of capacity cannot simply be assumed.

The Mental Capacity Act was designed to protect and support adults who lack the capacity to make their own decisions about their care or their medical treatment.

Everyone working in health and social care who acts on behalf of people who lack capacity have a duty to follow the provisions of the Mental Capacity Act.

The Mental Capacity Act also guides carers such as family members and can be a helpful framework for both Jack and Jill, Denis and Janet. If someone is appointed as attorney, then that person can act on someone's behalf when they no longer have the capacity to make a particular decision.

An attorney must always act in the individual's best interests, but a person must have capacity to arrange an LPA. This means that if Jack did not agree an LPA when he had capacity, this is no longer an option for him. Without an LPA to act in Jack's best interests – and usually selling their house to move near to family is in their best interests – Jill would have to apply to the Court of Protection for a court order appointing someone to act on Jack's behalf.

The Mental Capacity Act covers all decisions involving a person's care, from day-to-day decisions such as what to wear or eat to serious and life-changing decisions such as where to live, and medical treatment. All carers and professionals should know and follow the provisions of the Mental Capacity Act. The Act makes it clear that if a person lacks decision-making capacity, professionals should try to consult someone previously named by that person as close relatives, friends and carers.

The Mental Capacity Act Code of Practice clearly states that a diagnosis of dementia does not mean that the person lacks capacity. Indeed, the Mental Capacity Act begins from the assumption that every adult has the capability of making decisions for themselves. In the situation of Denis and Janet, Janet felt that Denis needed some support in his decision-making. Janet's strategy was to talk to Denis, involve him in thinking about his choices and offer alternatives.

Decision-making without involving the person living with dementia may have a negative impact, especially when somebody feels that they could have made the decision themselves. It may lead to feelings of frustration and powerlessness, and a loss of trust in the one who made the decision.

Decision-making

Decision-making can be a complicated process. The person may not recognise the need for a decision, or may not understand the options, risks or consequences. If memory has been significantly affected, it might not be possible for someone to draw on their own experience or to think creatively.

The starting point

- If someone has the capacity to decide for themselves, then they should be allowed to do so.
- Remember that someone may be able to make some decisions but not others.
- A frequent change of mind does not mean an inability to make a decision.
- If a person has capacity, they can make a wise and an unwise decision.
- As dementia progresses, the ability to make decisions will also change.

If the person does not have the capacity to make a specific decision, then perhaps one can be achieved if:

- they have more time;
- return to the issue later;
- the issue is presented differently;
- there is the help and support of a family member or good friend.

Shared decision-making

This ensures that an individual is involved as far as they are able in the decision-making process even if unable to make an independent or a supported choice.

Finally, if someone does not have capacity for this decision and cannot be supported, it can be made in their best interests, but it must be as minimally restrictive of their freedom as possible.

Some useful pointers

- Choose a time that works for the individual: for instance, if the person becomes tired in the afternoon, wait until the next day for a decision and choose a time of day when they are more alert.
- Support may include:
    - ◊ making sure the person can see and hear: for instance, checking hearing aids are working and is wearing the right glasses;
    - ◊ giving helpful information and explanations;
    - ◊ giving enough, or even extra, time;
    - ◊ talking things through with an expert or someone the person trusts.

The Mental Capacity Act is what is called "decision specific". In other words, does this person have the capacity to make this decision? It is crucial to ask what the decision is and to assess its importance.

Some decisions have serious consequences. Someone with dementia may not be too concerned about choices of clothing or food, but the accompanier could perhaps bring a jumper just in case the person changes their mind, or there may be other opportunities to eat more healthily. There may be more concern regarding possible serious consequences following an apparent decision not to have a particular medical treatment.

To support the person when making a more serious decision:

- does the person understand it?
- can they retain the information long enough to make a choice?
- can they weight up the consequences of making or not making the decision?
- can they communicate their conclusion?

In answering these questions, the accompanier could consider whether there is other information that could support somebody in making a decision, including information from another trusted source such as a doctor or family member, and checking for anything that might be influencing the person's decision. A good example here is if someone mistakenly thinks that a particular medical intervention means a long stay in hospital.

- If an individual has capacity for this particular decision, even one with serious consequences, then it is to be respected even if other people think it is unwise.
- If somebody's decision-making capacity is in doubt, then an appropriate person will need to carry out a capacity test.

A professional carer will find it important to record, in writing, the stages of this process. If there is any doubt, the involving of others, especially professionals, might be valuable.

- If someone is judged not to have capacity for this particular decision and cannot be supported in it, then any decision must be made in their best interests and must be the least restrictive option.

- Without planning and the use of good and timely communication, decisions might be needed at a point of crisis.

Communication

Good communication requires attentiveness, thoughtfulness and planning, especially if the conversation may be difficult for the individual or for the would-be communicator.

The SCARS framework, developed by people working in palliative and end-of-life care[3] might be useful.

SCARS stands for:

Setting

Communicate with kindness

Ask the person

Reflect on what the person says and respond

Summarise and then plan

- Ask if the person wants the presence of a trusted helper.
- Your reflection and response help to gauge what has been understood – not whether they understand what you want them to know, but what they understand by what is said.
- Effective communication can uncover what is important.

[3] https://www.difficultconversations.org.uk/

- Remember culture and language, especially if English is not someone's first language. Think about bringing in an interpreter to help.
- Pace the conversation: there may be a lot to process.
- Think about the timing of the conversation.
- If you are acting in a professional capacity, remember to follow the protocols of your organisation.
- Know your limits.

Good communication with people does not have to be only in words. We also use non-verbal interactions through gestures, smiles, touch, eye contact and attitudes. Gently holding somebody's hand and simple presence – even in silence – can can tell someone that they are valued and loved.

Maureen describes her experience of communication:

"One of the areas I was most determined to keep in place was that I would be the first face Mike saw each morning and the last face at night. After prayers, I prepared and fed Mike breakfast in bed before the initial daily care visits began at 8am. I always used a gentle tone of voice, reduced moving him needlessly and chatted cheerfully. I felt that touch was important. I would hold his hand often, wipe his face and hands myself and tell what the day would hold for us."

Strategies for living well with dementia

It should go without saying that it is essential to involve the person living with dementia in decisions about solutions to a difficulty, strategies for living well, or aids and assistance. This contribution will not only lead to a higher chance of success but is also a matter of acting ethically and affirming the person's human dignity. People living with dementia, just like everybody else, are different and have preferences. Some strategies work for some but not others; some might find one thing helpful which another person would find confusing. It is also important to bear in mind that skills and perceptions can change at different stages of dementia.

The Alzheimer's Society offer some key strategies in their *Memory Handbook.* [4]

- set up a daily routine;
- talk about your day;
- plan ahead;
- try to do just one thing at a time so that you can concentrate better;
- break up a task into small steps so that you can focus on one part at a time;
- ask for help if you need it;
- have one place for all the important things like keys, glasses and purse;
- keep things as clear and organised as you can by, for instance, labelling drawers and removing unnecessary things.

A common strategy is to have a recorded message that reminds the person to take their keys when they open the door to leave the house. This is sometimes a good idea but let's recall Sue and Joan's experiences. Sue installed a pull-cord voice alarm in her mother's house. She and the family felt reassured that their

[4] https://www.alzheimers.org.uk/sites/default/files/2020-03/The%20memory%20handbook%201540.pdf

mother, Joan would be safe and able to call for help especially if she fell. But Sue arrived one morning to find her mother petrified, convinced that there had been a man in the house during the night. Sue initially dismissed her mother's concern, thinking that she had probably left the television switched on or had heard someone in the street. However, a few days later Joan rang Sue to tell her that the walls were talking.

Sue also bought Joan a digital photograph frame where the photographs of family members changed automatically. Joan had always loved the countryside so Sue also included pictures of peaceful scenes of rivers and woodland. Soon Sue realised that her mother thought that the moving photographs were people who were physically present and that she was convinced that the river water would flow into her house.

We should not be afraid to try things out and to make changes if things do not work well.

Activities

A daily regular routine can be invaluable for helping people remember what will happen over the course of the day. But they also need other activities to make sure there is variety and interest in their lives.

Top of the list of activities for many people is simply having someone there who will spend time with them. But there are many interests that can really add to shared time together. It does not matter if it is not done perfectly or even not done particularly well. The point is to find something enjoyable: if it does not work then it is always possible to try something else.

It is important to begin from the person themselves. Not everyone likes to take walks and someone may not feel up to going out on this particular occasion. It is also critical to take account of what the individual can do. Talking afterwards about how the day has been, as Maureen did with Mike, is another way of remembering and feeling good about your activities.

Outdoor activities can involve light gardening, planting, watering or feeding the birds. The person may simply want to sit on a bench and watch the world go by or sit in the park. There are, however, things to consider: if somebody is relatively immobile or in a wheelchair, consider whether they might be be too hot or too cold. A person may not like sitting in the full sun or they may love it, so it is best to check – and watch out for sunburn.

For many people, pets make good companions and someone may find it easier to interact with an animal where there is no need for conversation or social skills.

Joan had always kept cats when she lived in her own home. Simply sitting in her care home with a cat on her knee made her much more relaxed and peaceful. However, not everyone likes animals and encouraging seemingly friendly dogs or cats may cause them to become fearful or anxious.

Some people seem to need to walk. Walking has many benefits, not least because it is good exercise, gets a person outdoors, relieves boredom and can be a social activity. Walking also helps keep someone independent.

A person living with dementia may feel the need to walk because:

- some of their needs are not being met;
- they have forgotten why they set out in the first place;
- they may be:
  - ◊ looking for something or someone;
  - ◊ unaware of the time;
  - ◊ restless or in pain.

If it often happens during the night, it may be due to:

- difficulty in sleeping;
- heightened need for the bathroom.

Helpful hints for planning ahead

Many activities are helped by planning:

- safety for walking – with or without walking aids or wheelchairs – to minimise stumbles and falls;
- garden seats if someone tires quickly;
- points of interest such as bird feeders, ornaments and raised beds;
- suitable clothing for longer walks and to cope with the weather;
- accompaniment for longer walks;
- some form of identification and emergency contact numbers for someone who is unaccompanied.

In a community where everyone knows each other, a carer may be able to rely on others to watch out for a person who is living with dementia. However, the individual's human dignity and right to privacy may require that certain aspects of their health, including a diagnosis of dementia, should be kept confidential.

If there is a justifiable cause for concern if someone insists on walking alone out of the house, it may be reasonable to lock them in. This is a difficult decision and might be risky in case of an accident or a fire.

The Mental Capacity Act reminds carers that when a person lacks capacity, a decision made in that person's best interests must be the least restrictive of the person's freedoms. A person can be locked in if:

- they consent;
- it is in their best interests;
- it is the least restrictive option for keeping them safe;
- they are not alone.

What do you think about locking someone in "for their safety"?

Feeding people

Feeding a person is a profoundly human activity. We care about the food we prepare for our loved ones. Food is physically, spiritually and socially nourishing. One of the most trusting things someone can do is to open their mouth and allow themselves to be fed.

Weight loss in dementia

As dementia progresses weight loss becomes inevitable and this is not necessarily a signal of neglect.

- The very activity of eating may become a chore.
- The choices of food may be overwhelming.
- They may forget:

◊ to eat;
◊ that they have already eaten;
◊ to drink sufficient fluids.

They may no longer recognise:

◊ tastes or textures;
◊ what they are being offered as food.

- They may have a sore mouth but not tell carers.

A few tips

- Encourage a varied and balanced diet; be flexible with preferences.
- Encourage the drinking of plenty of fluids: a good strategy is to offer small amounts throughout the day.
- Check that dentures fit properly and that the person is not in pain from, for instance, mouth ulcers or toothache.
- If somebody has poor eyesight, they may not see a glass or that it contains water. Think about introducing coloured liquid.
- Some people find it difficult to distinguish between the food, the plate, the tablecloth and all the utensils on a table. Keep things simple and try to avoid too many patterns or colours.
- Ensure that food and drink is placed easily and safely within reach.
- Think about the environment: is the person comfortable? Is the chair suitable? Can they see the plate? Is there a calm environment or are there too many distractions?
- Some people are not aware of temperatures so check that the food is not too hot.

- If the person has lost their appetite, consider whether this could be the result of medication, lack of exercise, a sore mouth or perhaps even depression?
- Give the person time and allow them to be as independent as they can be. To maintain independence, consider feeding aids such as bended straws, large-handled spoons and rimmed plates or bowls. Offer finger food.
- Make mealtimes a social activity.
- Consider making a dental appointment.

Often good strategies come out of personal experience. Sue noticed that, at mealtimes, Joan only ate half of her plate of food. She initially thought that Joan had eaten enough. Then she discovered that if she turned the plate around, her mother would eat the other half of the meal. It seemed that Joan's poor peripheral vision prevented her from seeing the contents of the whole plate.

Sue realised that Joan was more likely to drink if she were given orange squash since she could see there was something in the glass. On the days when Joan said she did not feel like eating, Sue would suggest that they went into the day room for a cup of tea and piece of cake or nibbles while they chatted – this distraction seemed to work very well.

Sue saw that Joan enjoyed eating curry, something she had always previously refused. Some textures seemed to cause problems such that Joan would spit out things like peas, carrot pieces and beans. Mashing these vegetables helped: they did not feel like inedible objects.

Of course, helping people with eating needs particular attention and care must be taken when people find swallowing increasingly difficult. Preparing soft food and cutting food into smaller pieces may help but whole grapes and nuts may cause problems. A dysphagia team, who specialise in swallowing problems may be able to offer useful suggestions.

Memory boxes

Memory boxes are easy to create. A memory box contains items that the person living with dementia finds meaningful. These items can give comfort and can become a talking point and point of connection with other people. It may simply find pleasure in sorting through the box. Talking with someone and their family or carers about what matters to them, and what to include, makes the experience personal and gives people a sense of owning the project. It is equally important to be careful not to include items that may bring unhappy or painful memories.

Quite often family members may discover that their loved one has kept things that they had never realised before were important, which can give an additional insight into that person. Moreover, the creative activity of making a memory box may encourage the making of other boxes about different life events or memories.

Memory boxes can contain whatever has resonance with the person. Some relevant things may be related to the person's previous job, hobbies, souvenirs from holidays or mementos, photographs, letters and even music or scented items like *pot pourri,* dried flowers and lavender.

The purpose of a memory box includes the regular handling of its contents. If this is likely to damage items such as photographs and letters, copies of the originals might be more usefully kept in the box. With increasing reliance on touch and other senses, a memory box with different textures and sensory stimulus can be very appealing.

Of course, in creating a memory box we must use practical wisdom.

- It should be:
    - ◊ sufficiently robust to allow for regular use;
    - ◊ a suitable size for the person to lift, hold and store;
    - ◊ about the size of a shoebox (12in x 9in; 30cm x 22cm) with a lid that is easy to open.
- If an item is rare or unique it may be better to leave it out.
- Sharp, dangerous or heavy objects should be avoided.
- Removing pins from jewellery may avoid injury.
- Label items with string tags rather than less permanent adhesive labels.
- Including a paper list of items with an explanation of their relevance might help the person to recognise something and understand its presence.
- Labels also help family and carers to make connections and encourage the conversation.

Bel, a memory support worker who provides people and families with information about how to make memory boxes and create life stories, explains that she offers a range of different approaches so that people can choose what works for them. After all, she says, "In dementia there is no one size fits all!"

It may also be a matter of trial and error and the idea behind memory boxes can be expanded. For instance, Jackie went to great lengths to make up a memory box of photographs and small mementoes for her mother. Her mother was not interested in this collection of special memories, but she loved to have a box full of different coloured threads – she had always made clothes for her children and handling the threads perhaps brought back fond memories.

We may want to reflect on what some people hope memory boxes may achieve. Many people see them as a method of reminiscence therapy. Exploring treasured items with someone else may help encourage long-and short-term memory. However, the main purpose of memory boxes is simply to enjoy moments, either with others or in private. Memory boxes do not suit everyone and if a person becomes upset or frustrated, then clearly it is not fulfilling its purpose and is no longer needed.

Photographs

Looking through photographs can be a rewarding and enjoyable activity for everyone.

Putting together different photograph albums can be a creative activity for all concerned and it gives the opportunity to share memories.

Photographs arranged:

- in chronological order illustrate someone's life story;
- can raise interesting conversations about the past;
- of special events or particular people help to vary the experience;

- to show various hobbies or occupations can reflect what the person likes to do.

We may want to reflect on what we hope to achieve with photographs. Sue explains, "My mother could not cope with photographs. I know her eyesight was not good. But I think the real problem was that she became distressed because she couldn't name the people in the pictures. It was as if she thought it was a test which she kept on failing."

Think about enjoying photographs as a way of reminiscing rather than remembering. Reminiscing is about looking back, often with fondness. Remembering is about memory recall. Making comments like, "You look very happy in this photograph" or "You look very young here" help to make connections. Try not to correct them and be aware that some photographs may bring up painful memories. Be sensitive to their reactions and if photographs cause distress, then try a different activity.

Sensory triggers

We often forget that our senses of touch, taste, sight, hearing, and smell can carry powerful emotions. We can use objects as sensory triggers: the smell of flowers or perfume can not only be pleasurable, but they can also bring back or create memories; the touch of something soft can bring comfort; handling materials can help relieve boredom and can also help with maintaining hand movement and co-ordination; listening to the world and seeing nature can be uplifting.

However, daily living can become more of a challenge if a person has sensory loss. Moreover, life can become very frightening if a person's senses are negatively affected by the way in which the brain is interpreting signals. Sometimes giving people time to process what is going on may help; at other times it may be necessary to take a walk or leave the room for a while to avoid sensory overload.

We often underestimate how sensory stimulus can increase levels of anxiety, anger, irritation and even feelings of isolation. Family and carers need to be alert to someone's sensory challenges in case they are feeling overwhelmed.

Touch: sometimes people lose a sense of what is hot and cold. They might:

- feel the cold more;
- not realise that a drink or the tap water is too hot;
- want to hold hands or hug more than previously.

Think about:

- asking if another layer of clothing is needed;
- checking the temperature of food and drink;
- fitting temperature-sensitive taps.

Taste and smell: these two senses are often linked, especially when it comes to food.

- Some people find that food has become tasteless or is very bland.
- Mealtimes become boring.
- New tastes are often developed, e.g. for spicy food.
- Food may not smell right.

- A smell may remind a person of something that they would rather forget.

Think about:

- sharing what is happening;
- be open to new things.

Seeing: There might be difficulty in seeing, not because of sight impairment, but because the brain is incorrectly interpreting messages from the eyes.

- A line might appear as a step or a step as a line and might present as an obstacle to be climbed or a potential hazard.
- Straight lines might no longer appear straight and might appear to have dips or bumps in them.
- Changed depth perception might cause difficulties in judging the depth of a step when descending.
- A black carpet may "look like" a hole.
- Uniformly coloured walls and doors may cause difficulty in finding a way out of a room.
- A shiny surface may produce a reflection that the person does not recognise.
- Poor light can create shadows or shadowy figures.
- Coloured surfaces may "look like" there are things on the floor or table which need to be picked up.

Think about:

- checking glasses and vision, perhaps asking for specialist advice;

- reducing shadows by bright and even lighting;
- considering décor so that everything does not look the same colour.

In the event of sight problems due to the presence of one or more cataracts which might be successfully and easily removed, it is important to consider other practicalities.

Can the person:

- understand the need for cataract surgery and its physical constraints?
- cope with:
  - ◊ the unfamiliar hospital environment?
  - ◊ surgery under local anaesthetic? (The operation typically lasts for approximately 7-10 minutes and so a general anaesthetic is highly unlikely.)
  - ◊ wearing an eye shield overnight for at least one night?
  - ◊ four subsequent weeks of eye drops?
  - ◊ following instructions such as not rubbing the affected eye?

With good communication with the medical team, it can be ascertained whether the operation is in the person's overall best interests or whether the treatment would be too burdensome for them.

Hearing: some people become oversensitive to sounds and what was once pleasurable may become noise. Some sounds evoke frightening memories.

- A sudden loud noise can cause alarm.
- The testing of fire alarms:
  - ◊ can bring back terrifying wartime memories;
  - ◊ might be seen as indicating a fire rather than the testing of an alarm.
- Music shops, for instance, can be distracting or irritating, especially if someone cannot work out the music's reason, source or direction.
- Noisy environments may make hearing conversations difficult. This is not necessarily helped if the other person shouts to make themselves heard.
- Many competing sounds, even if they are everyday noises, can cause the person to feel overwhelmed and so lead to increased anxiety or anger.

Think about:

- visiting a specialist to check hearing and to check for example, ringing sounds (tinnitus);
- attentive listening and reflecting back to the person what they have said;
- time for recovery or 'time out';
- seating in order to reduce the volume of sound;
- with planned fire alarm testing:

- ◊ give several advance warnings of its date and timing;
- ◊ ensure that someone is not left alone during the test – especially if the alarm might accidentally trigger memories of the Blitz or other traumatic experiences;
- ◊ if possible and without causing possible future risks, switch off the sound in the room where the person concerned is located (many devices have flashing lights which, independently of sound, indicate that they are in working order);
- ◊ inform the tester if the sound has been temporarily switched off in a particular location.

Assistive technology and smart technology

With advances in online communication distance need not be so much of a barrier to communication.

Maureen explains, "Our son and family living in Austria used FaceTime to speak and share stories with us several times each week. Again, he [Mike] rallied when the young ones had spoken to him."

In addition to communication, assistive technology helps to keep people independent, safe and active. There are many new and exciting technologies that are being promoted to help people live well and independently. There are now technologies that can make homes dementia-friendly. Some of these:

- regulate room temperature;
- are movement-sensitive, alarms and monitors;
- everyday household devices that "talk" to each other;
- play music;
- operate the television;
- remind people to take their medication;
- help people stand and move;
- are interactive.

However, not everyone has access to technologies and some technologies are expensive and beyond a person's budget. Many people have neither the information nor the training to make good use of technologies.

An overreliance on technology might:

- lessen awareness of a person's genuine needs;
- reduce personal contact with the person living with dementia;
- restrict someone's freedom of movement.

While telephone and contact services have proved successful in helping to reduce loneliness, people are especially concerned that moves towards telemedicine and telecare systems, where patients are seen remotely by specialists, may become the norm instead of face-to-face care.

It may be a relief for a carer to know where their loved one is by using smart phones, tracking devices or wearable technology such as electronic tags in clothes or technology that monitor exercise, activity and heart rate. Such devices may give useful information but, ethically, there is a real question here about obtaining consent for their use.

The other thing to consider is whether a technology is appropriate to someone and their circumstances, and whether it helps meet individual needs. What one person finds useful another may find unhelpful.

There may be an advantage in timely experimentation with a particular technology to see if it works for the people concerned within a given situation. Assessment and familiarity with equipment might enable the longer use of helpful technologies.

Assistive technologies have great potential as part of a range of complementary strategies to help people live well, provided they do not substitute for what makes a genuine difference: good personal care, dementia friends and dementia-friendly communities.

Visiting and the importance of friends

Maureen and Mike found their friends an invaluable source of support. As Maureen recounts,

"Every Tuesday morning for three years (pre-covid) a small group of friends from the SVP and the Catenians collected Mike, took him by car to local beauty spots for a two-hour walk (latterly pushed his wheelchair) and chatted. Mike was always very animated on his return. His friends also related Mike's efforts to join in with the banter."

Of course, covid made socialising more difficult but not impossible.

"Our daughter and family in the town visited at least weekly. Once covid arrived and any exchanges with our daughter were on the doorstep, it was only carers and medics who entered our home. I recall in October 2020, when we celebrated our Golden Wedding anniversary, twelve friends appeared with flowers and gifts at the front window. I could move Mike's recliner chair nearer so he could see and hear them. Mike's oldest friend and wife visited every Thursday morning to talk to him through the window. These communications were a great comfort to both Mike and to me. As Mike's condition progressed and his interactions were so greatly reduced, I tried to keep him positive but he greatly valued the diversity of visitors, particularly that of male company and conversation."

Rhoda offers some advice on visiting:

"If someone wants to become a dementia visitor, I suggest they read information and advice online and talk to others doing this. They could perhaps attend some training if they can. Mostly, they will need to learn as they go along as each person is very different."

Helpful hints for visiting

Apart from those special occasions, and depending on the individual, one or two visitors at a time is probably about right.

- Regular visitors should think about coming at a time when someone is at their best and be sure not to overstay their welcome.

- Reduce distractions, for instance, switching off the television – with permission – may make the visit more fruitful.
- It may be helpful to introduce yourself even if you think the person knows who you are.
- Be friendly and positive, speaking at an appropriate pace and not too loudly, giving people time to respond and not rushing the conversation, are all good practice.
- Sometimes, going with the flow of the conversation and entering the reality of the moment, even if the chat does not appear to make sense, is a good demonstration of friendship.
- Perhaps devise an activity – or bring one – or ask the person what they would like to do.

A visitor's guest book:

- may be a reminder of who has been to visit;
- can be seen when visitors have gone;
- a good point of conversation for subsequent visitors;
- encourage visitors to write the date of the visit, their names, how they spent their time with the person and, if possible, say when they will come next.

Memory cafés and social groups

Social groups that cater for both a family member or carer and their loved one, and groups just for the person living with dementia, can be real lifelines. Maureen and Mike together attended an Alzheimer's Society group called Singing for the Brain.

Mike also attended a group called Together, run by a local church and to the local authority day care centre, The Homestead. Maureen says,

"Mike enjoyed all aspects of the groups. The variety of activities, particularly at the Together group, was very stimulating. The agenda took into consideration the time of year, current events and anniversaries and kept those able to move about doing so. At both venues Mike danced at every opportunity with me or whoever he could. He was never distressed but could get tired and a bit sleepy towards the end."

Mike had "great fun" at The Homestead, where "snooker, table tennis, dining, dancing, visits from entertainers and a respite dog were part of the agenda".

Memory cafés are designed for both the person living with dementia and their carer to share activities together. Activities vary from café to café but, significantly, they give people the opportunity to talk with people who are in similar situations and can be the source of valuable local information. Successful memory cafés tend to provide a quiet environment in a relaxed setting.

As things get hard

Everyone goes through hard times now and then. Our exploration of living well with dementia would not be real if it did not also include some of the challenges that life brings.

Coping strategies

People often unconsciously develop their own coping strategies, whether it is taking a long walk when under stress, getting engrossed in a hobby or having a cup of tea with a friend. Undoubtedly, knowing well the person living with dementia helps in aiding them to work out coping strategies.

Maureen realised that, for Mike, plenty of activities and distractions made things go more smoothly. She also noticed that it became important to avoid topics that would make him uncomfortable and this included both direct questions and decision-making. Maureen realistically pointed out to us that a person's personality influences coping strategies. As she explains, the "downside" of avoiding certain topics "was exacerbated because Mike had a very withdrawn personality and would often keep worries to himself throughout our fifty-year marriage so, as with everything connected to dementia care, one can only do what they judge to be best."

Maureen also reminded us of the need to consider carers and family when it comes to coping strategies. She found the kind of things that made a difference were finding timely and appropriate professional help, having friends and welcoming their views, concerns and suggestions, having opportunities to undertake activities like a coffee with friends while Mike was occupied elsewhere and, of course, prayers. It is also important for the carer to continue their personal interests. Maureen found that baking, reading and working in the garden were good ways to help restore a bit of balance. And as Maureen adds, "lots of taking deep breaths" and "staying positive wherever possible".

Truth-telling and appreciating people's realities

Dementia can make a person feel isolated even when with other people. This is especially so when surrounded by confusing moments, when people seem to wander in and out of life, speaking in ways that are not understood, and doing things for or to them. Their capacity to feel and relate to other people may seem stronger than before, their senses apparently playing tricks on them. It can be scary.

For those accompanying the person, when it comes to sorting out the fact from the fiction, it may be better to focus on the feelings rather than the facts. Feelings of fear, insecurity or anxiety are true even if the fact that, for instance, the person's bag has been stolen, is not. An imagined memory may be based on something else and it may be a way of making sense of it. For Bel, truth-telling and appreciating people's realities is "always at the heart of what we [dementia friends] strive to do". How to deal with realities and truth-telling is a significant issue.

There are occasions when a carer or family member should not conclude that "it's the dementia speaking", especially when it refers to "things going missing". Sadly, pilfering happens, as does cheating with, for instance, the cost of shopping for the person living with dementia. Sometimes the concerns are genuine and merit an immediate response.

Similarly, some events have simple explanations which can immediately ease the anxiety. For example, a deeply worried complaint that "the bed is rocking from side-to-side" was, once again, not "the dementia speaking". The cause was the unfamiliar action of an electronically operated inflatable ripple mattress which had been given to someone who was bedridden. It was easily explained as "a very special mattress to help you to feel comfortable in bed".

As Maureen explains,

"I have read many books, looked online for solutions and opinions and considered many scenarios to assist my reactions to the people with dementia with whom I came into contact. Generally, I used avoidance strategies and changed the subject when given an option. As an example,

Mike liked looking at himself in our lounge mirror when we danced. On one occasion, I said, 'How old are you?', Mike replied that he was forty (he was sixty-seven). I said 'Wow! That's great! That makes me thirty-eight' – and we moved on!"

For Joan, old information seemed to be new and if the conversation turned to her father or mother she would suddenly cry over their deaths as if she had heard the news for the first time. Sue found this distressing and, whenever one of these episodes occurred, she initially told her mother that they had died more than fifty years previously. Sue was particularly upset that Joan appeared to have forgotten her marriage to Sue's father and did not seem to mourn him. After a while, Sue changed her strategy and, whenever Joan became tearful, would ask her about happy memories of her parents. Sue also found that she could talk to Joan about her own father. The memory was still there, although distantly.

Often certain behaviours are, in fact, attempts at communication. A person may not be able to express a need from hunger and thirst, to pain or boredom, needing the toilet or needing security. Yet their search for a long-dead mother, fear that something has been lost or simply reaching out, may express a deeper reality. How we ourselves see reality is often complicated so we should not think that this is not the same for people with dementia. Although we may want to help keep someone in touch with reality, empathising with their genuine feelings and embracing their reality may lead us towards new horizons.

Rhoda's experience of her father's sense of reality may have resonance with many people:

"My dad rarely gets very aggressive or difficult to deal with, but he has many hallucinations which lead him to walk around or do things which are related to his current reality. For instance, he thought the care home was on fire so he found a fire alarm and set it off (obviously this would be the best thing to do if the home had been burning), which resulted in the fire brigade attending! Obviously, this was disruptive for the care home but, as far as I can see, the staff were fairly understanding.

When he first moved into the home, he sometimes tried to go out. All occasions were linked to his thinking he needed to go somewhere. I think he has now settled down and understands that he only goes out when someone is with him.

The main difficulty which occurs is when he thinks something distressing is happening. These are some recurring ones: on several occasions he has thought he is going bankrupt or hasn't enough money to pay people. At other times he has thought I was going away or going abroad and wouldn't be coming to see him again. Another recurring theme is a belief that he has been told he needs to move out at very short notice and he doesn't know how he to sort out the details. In between these hallucinations he has others which are less distressing, although perhaps sometimes annoying. He also has 'neutral', interesting or enjoyable ones, such as his involvement in filming for a TV programme or having tea with old friends."

At times Rhoda finds this distressing. She feels, "I do need to counteract this at least to some level in order to help him get past it if possible." Recognising that these issues are significant for her father, Rhoda has developed ways to address these issues "gently but firmly, giving rational reasons to show him why" something is not so.

"If it is not of great importance, I will not disagree directly with him, but if he is distressed, I will address the issue, for example in reply to those mentioned: if he thinks he is going bankrupt, I will tell him I have looked at the bank account recently and could see that he has enough money and that there is no need to worry. I reassure him that if there were a problem, the family would help him. If he says I am going away and not coming back, I tell him clearly, gently and firmly that I am not going away; I am still living in my house (I tell him the address) and I wouldn't move because I want to come and see him every week, I wouldn't leave him. If he thinks he must move out, I say that I think he is staying in this room for the moment, that the care home hasn't said anything and that they would have let me know if there were to be any change. This doesn't always work, so if I am at the home I will say 'Well, it looks like you have got all your things in here at the moment – here is your bed, here are your clothes, here are your photographs, so I think you are staying here tonight anyway and we will sort out the rest tomorrow.'"

As Rhoda points out, her father,

"Has so many 'happenings' that if you were to try and bring him back to our reality all the time, you would be constantly contradicting him, something which has no good outcome for anyone. He is aware that some of these concerns are not real, but not usually until after they have happened.

I have got used to the fact that if he is relating something that happened to him earlier, he will tell it as if it did happen (like you would tell someone a dream or a story) even if he has realised it wasn't real. For instance, he would say 'I went to Ireland today', or 'I was in London and saw Prince Charles'. Closer to home he could have been to Ulleskelf, Batley or somewhere in Leeds.

My response varies according to how he seems to be feeling about the experience. For instance, when he told me he had been in New York or Ireland and seemed to have enjoyed it, I commented, 'Well you get about more than I do!' If he mentions being with somebody (whom I know he hasn't seen for a long time) then I might say 'Well, you haven't seen them for a long time, have you?'

He often thinks my younger brother has been around the place, so I don't usually counteract that unless it would interfere with real events in some way. When he tells me a story about what has been happening, I usually just say 'oh yes', 'Aha', 'Oh, really?', 'That must have been interesting', or something else which allows him to continue with retelling the incident just like you would want someone to do for you if you were retelling an incident or even a dream.

There are times when I have had to go along with a story and say something which would fit within it even though it isn't true (because it affected what needed to happen next in real life), but I avoid doing this if possible. For instance, on one occasion when I went to visit him, he was most concerned that all the people had arrived for the board meeting and he didn't even have the agenda ready. I was trying to persuade him that it was time to sit and have a chat with me but, for him, there was a group of people waiting to have this meeting (a reference to his previous work). I found myself saying 'I think they are going away now, it's O.K.' to which he motioned to the 'people' to tell them to go."

Rhoda's common-sense approach can be summed up as "I think the main thing to help in communication is to try to understand and be empathetic to what is going on for the person living with dementia and think how you would want to be treated or spoken to if you were them." Her advice is:

"I always try to be cheerful and show I am pleased to see him or speak with him. I will give him my attention and look at him with a smile. I have found that he can pick up very easily on body language (even when I think he hasn't noticed) if I am distracted or worried about something else. I have learned not to look away a lot or fidget when waiting for him to speak but maintain a listening stance. I will try to get the conversation going with a general question or comment, 'How are you doing?' 'What's happening?' but this might not be right for everyone with dementia.

I encourage him to tell me the story even though I might not understand what he is talking about (this is especially true on the phone because the Parkinson's makes him speak quietly). If I can see that he is just wanting to tell me something that happened or is happening, I will make encouraging interjections to let him know I am listening and will do my best to find some thread in the story that makes sense or maybe that I can pick up and link to something I know did happen in the past.

I think it is important that he feels he is listened to, and that he is having a conversation. When he pauses, it is usually because he is trying to find a word (this is becoming more frequent), so I will wait, or if I think it might help to jog his memory and I have followed the train of thought sufficiently I will suggest a word 'Did you mean X?', or ask a question which might help to get at what he meant. He usually welcomes this rather than getting frustrated with it, but I would never labour the point if it is not forthcoming.

I will tell him a bit about my day or something that has happened to me that he would find interesting, like seeing an unusual bird. I will also tell him a bit about the family, but not too many things at once as he can get them confused. I will repeat things as if it were the first time I have told him. I will tell him what day it is and what time it is to help him feel orientated, although it doesn't always match with what he thinks! I use photographs or memories to start a conversation about things from the past, as this is easier than trying to talk about the present."

Some tips

- Agree with the person's feelings – which are genuine. Never argue.
- Redirect. Never reason.
- Distract. Never shame.
- Reassure. Never lecture.
- Reminisce. Never say "remember".
- Repeat. Never say "I already told you".
- Say "do what you can". Never "you can't".
- Ask. Never command.
- Encourage and praise. Never condescend.
- Reinforce. Never force.

When care becomes hard and requires hard decisions

One of the greatest difficulties is knowing who to turn to when things get hard. Many people can turn to family and friends for a break or just to chat, but sometimes the help of professionals in needed. As Bel points out, "it helps to give out phone numbers which people can call for help".

Everyone's experience is different, but as Rhoda says, we try to do the best we can. The help of friends, family and professionals is vital.

"Although I haven't had some of the very stressful experiences that other people have had when caring for family members with dementia (for instance they go out and get into danger, or they are very aggressive and won't accept help), it is always hard to see the changes in the family member and sometimes feel at a loss as to how to help or reassure them when they are distressed. In addition, you are always questioning whether you are doing the best for them and whether you could have done more, wishing that they had a better quality of life. I always pray for my dad and put him into God's hands as he loves him deeply. I talk with my family, my brothers and my friends about what is happening and how I am feeling. Friends who have had similar experiences are especially helpful."

Making the decision that a person's needs would be better taken care of in a different setting like a care home is possibly one of the hardest decisions families and carers may have to make. Frequently this decision comes about gradually, and what to do becomes a matter of good practical sense: as Sue explains.

"There were four of us children and we were all concerned about our mother. It became very clear that she was not coping well in her own house. Our mother had always lived with other people and the first time she had ever lived alone was after the death of our father. After his death our mother had moved into supported living accommodation. She managed for a year or so but was very lonely, even if she went to church every morning. She was very dependent on her car just to get her out of the house. After a series of 'near misses', we persuaded her to give up driving as she simply was not safe, but she seemed to become more and more isolated.

There was no way any of us could move into her little house because we all had children and jobs. For the same reason, she could not move in with one of us. On the days she did visit each of us, it was always very difficult because she was so restless and worried. She just was not happy.

Then she began to feel afraid in the house on her own. She did not like having 'strangers', carers around, started losing track of her medication, of where she was, what time it was, and was not having proper meals. We all thought that she would be safer and better looked after in a care home. We found a home near the church and our mother agreed to try it out for a bit.

To begin with, some of the parishioners used to visit but these visits soon tailed off. I suppose her friends were also getting old. I also think they found it difficult making conversation. Our mother always seemed to be anxious. She said that things were going missing and that she was being kept in. She was worrying all the time. But, on the other hand, she was looking better because she was eating proper meals and her medication was under control."

Of course, the decision to move to a care home should be made by the person themselves. But often by the time a person living with dementia has reached the stage when they need extra support and care, they no longer have the capacity to make this decision for themselves. If they have not appointed an attorney to make the decision then the decision can be made by their family or people close to them in conversation with health and social care professionals. This ensures that any decision is made in someone's best interests, and they should be involved in the decision-making process as far as is possible.

If somebody does not have any family or close friends then, in England and Wales, the local authority can appoint an Independent Mental Capacity Advocate to act on their behalf.

In Joan's case, the family explored other options such as supported living. Had she been living with one of her children, respite care might have been a possibility. However, a move to a care home seemed to be in Joan's best interests.

Moving a loved one to a care home does not mean to say that you give up caring. You may also have mixed feelings, or feelings of inadequacy or guilt. If you have looked after a person on a day-to-day basis, doing everything for them, you may find you are at a loss when the caring responsibilities have greatly lessened and you may miss the person. Finding people to talk to can be an invaluable support. It is worth finding out if the care home has group support for family and friends. It may also be possible to become involved in activities at the care home.

Accompanying people

Having explored some of the ways in which people can live well with dementia and how people can adjust to their new realities, we can summarise some of our reflections for people who accompany those living with dementia.

1. Know the person – as they are now and also their life story, or as much as they wish to share. This will help others understand why an individual responds as they do. A change in behaviour may indicate a problem that needs to be addressed.

2. Check on the basics: people need to feel safe, know that they will be cared for, have a sense of belonging and relationship with others, know they can make choices and to have a sense of achievement. Above all, people need to know they are significant and are valued.

3. Reflect on my own attitude to the person living with dementia and how my attitude may affect that person.

4. Reflect on my behaviour: being kind, respectful, asking permission, saying sorry, please and thank you, listening attentively, respecting privacy.

5. Remember that being with someone can be as effective as doing things for or with them.

Creating dementia-friendly communities

We have looked at what it means to live well with dementia and how people can be supported. However, our project is more ambitious: it is how everyone can contribute to helping people live well and includes the contributions of people living with dementia. Dementia-friendly communities are not simply a practical development to enable people to enjoy activities or to stay in their own homes. Certainly, providing support to people to stay at home and to live well is invaluable.

Dementia-friendly communities are more than this. A community is dementia-friendly when people with dementia are accepted as they are, when they are understood, respected and supported.

The community comes together in a joint enterprise. As Bel explains "networking and communities working together with local support agencies and parish councils" are the basis for creating dementia-friendly communities. Becoming a dementia-friendly community involves education, not only about different forms of dementia, but also about how to have a positive and realistic discussion about the condition. Being dementia-friendly is about being creative and thinking "outside the box", so that living in the present and living by the heart become natural. It is about encouraging others also to be dementia-friendly.

Rhoda talks about the supportive community Growing Old Grace-fully, a small charity working across the Diocese of Leeds, that supports dementia friends.[5] She explains that the vison of the charity is "that older people across the Catholic Diocese of Leeds experience spiritual, emotional and physical wellbeing in positive and inclusive parish communities".

As with many charities, Growing Old Grace-fully relies on volunteers who have other duties and commitments. The charity runs dementia friends' sessions in parishes across the diocese and helps with the dementia-friendly application process. It points people in the direction of other local resources, good information, and advice and alerts them to events such as Alzheimer's Day in September, Dementia Prayer Week in March and Dementia Action Week in May. It can also send out regular mailings with additional information. Growing Old Grace-fully

5 https://www.growingoldgracefully.org.uk/

organises specific themes for certain periods of time and seeks to inform good practice. In Rhoda's experience, "It is good to work together with the group, especially if there is a mix of people involved who all have different skills, experiences and links to networks. Each person is invaluable and brings their own contributions." Moreover, Rhoda says that people involved in the charity who are personally on their own dementia journey bring invaluable insights.

And the gaps

We have explored some of the things that help people to live well with dementia given the realities of the condition but Bel identified a major gap in "a good experience of good end-of-life care." This is where we turn in the next chapter.

Reflections for the reader:

What works for you?

What else do you need and want?

Chapter 4

And at the end

At our first meeting to discuss what sort of resource we would find helpful and so the type of resource we would like to produce, the Caritas Leeds Dementia Group was clear from the outset that the tone should focus on living well with dementia. At the same time the team's experience encompassed accompanying people with dementia and their families through dying, death and bereavement.

Clearly, every person has unique needs, their own wishes, values and ways of approaching the world. Moreover, everybody has the right to dignity and respect. This includes being involved in decisions about treatment, and how and where they wished to receive care. Thus, any reflection on dying, death and bereavement can only be spoken about in general terms. But since death is a part of life, living well with dementia also includes dying well. Therefore, we have included dying well in this book.

Approaching the end

We introduced the story of Maureen and Mike at the beginning of this book. In this chapter we hear from Maureen again as Mike reached the end of his journey.

Maureen and Mike: at home

"On 8 March 2021 Mike, my husband of 50 years, passed away as peacefully as I could hope, in bed in our home after an eleven-and-a half-year struggle with mixed dementia and, latterly, complications relating to his general health.

Three months earlier, the local GP, district nursing team and his carers had suggested that a palliative nurse from our local hospice was required to become involved in Mike's treatment either at home or in the hospice. I knew his wishes were to be at home, thought about the impact, made enquiries with family, friends, professionals and, shortly afterwards, the weekly visits from our nurse began.

Procedures were soon changed. The regular routine of hoisting Mike from his bed into the recliner chair in our lounge was considered too stressful and less safe for Mike and the care team. They approached me to ask if they could organise his care needs all in one room. This was very challenging as what limited distractions and entertainment we had were in the lounge, including access to a window where he could see family or friends as visitors since coronavirus was still very much with us in January 2021 and we had not then been vaccinated.

The next change was the method of morphine administration from oral to injections and then, in Mike's final month, to a syringe driver. On 5 March, Mike began to breathe strangely, with a pronounced rattling sound. I was told that this was because his organs were beginning to shut down. I asked if it caused him pain or distress and was advised that it was only distressing for those watching it happen. On the evening prior to Mike's death, the district nurses made their regular visit to "top up" the morphine. As they pulled the bedcovers back, I noticed that the flesh from his ankles and continuing up his legs was turning blue. I was very scared. For the previous weeks, I had slept in his room in a recliner chair but on 7 March, I decided to climb into his hospital bed with Mike and hold him in my arms. Half-in and half-out, I clung onto Mike, alternating between praying, speaking to him and dozing. It was very peaceful. My daughter and grandsons in Huddersfield had been with us all day, returning home around 7.45pm. At 1.58am, I stirred and noticed Mike had fallen silent. We stayed, still wrapped around each other, until I rang my daughter, 111 and the undertaker, so the process of putting his body to rest could begin shortly afterwards."

Maureen's experience is a good reminder that thinking ahead, for instance about where a person wants to be at the end, can really help when there are so many other decisions to be made.

As Maureen later pointed out, Mike had received the sacrament of the sick some six months previously and so spiritually, she felt that they were prepared. She had had the time to discuss things with family, friends and professionals and a plan had been put in place so that Mike could die at home. Of course, there were challenges, but good communication with professionals can help people adapt and adjust to the situation as it changes. It is hardly surprising that Maureen was worried and afraid at times – after all, for most of us being with a loved one who is dying is a totally new and emotionally draining time. Maureen's experience shows the importance of having professionals who can explain what is happening and be at hand if needed.

It is important to acknowledge that some people would find it too difficult to be alone with their dying loved one. Some may want to remember the person in a different way and so do not want to be there at the moment of death. This simply reflects the way in which everybody is different and deals with difficult situations in their own way. At the same time, it is important to speak to family, friends and professionals because you too need care as the person you care for approaches the end.

In the final analysis Maureen has beautifully and tenderly expressed her last moments with Mike who was clearly at peace and very much loved. The death of a loved one, even when expected, always comes as a shock, however much we try to prepare. But to be able to look back and say that the end came "as peacefully as I could hope" is surely a great blessing.

It is worth remembering that:

- Someone might not want those closest to them to see them die. It is a common experience that someone will breathe their last when, for instance, a family member visits the bathroom or goes to make themselves a hot drink. There is no need for feelings of guilt: it often seems that a dying person has chosen to wait for that moment of solitude.
- The custom of praying the Rosary aloud at the bedside of someone who is dying might or might not be a comfort, so sensitivity is needed. By way of example, one Sister suddenly became alert and declared, in no uncertain terms, "I don't want to hear any more Rosaries!"

- Hearing is said to be the last sense to be lost, so although someone might appear comatose and unresponsive, they might still be able to hear, so it's important that family members are able to tell them of their love.

Sue and Joan: in the care home

We met Joan and her daughter Sue in previous chapters.

After eighteen months in the care home, Joan's health had seriously declined and the home manager called Sue to tell her that she thought her mother was nearing the end. Sue takes up the story.

"I suppose we had been expecting this to come for a long time. Our mother had been becoming decreasingly responsive to us and less inclined to walk. When she first moved into the care home, she walked all the time and the staff had difficulty getting her to stay still. She did not want to eat and often left her tea to get cold.

Mum began sleeping a great deal until she was eventually in bed all the time. The manager explained that she was drifting in and out of consciousness. We had a discussion with the management team about what would be best for our mother. We all agreed that she would not want to be in hospital and so we agreed that the carer team would keep her comfortable in the care home. It was nice because we could come and go throughout the day and we could stay at night.

We arranged that two of us would always be in our mother's room on a rota basis. We played some quiet music that we knew our mother would like and chatted to each other over photographs and memories as we waited. The priest had given her the Sacrament of the Sick a few weeks before. Because she was not awake, our mother could not eat or drink. We were worried about this, but the duty nurse explained that this was a part of the natural dying process. She suggested we dip a cotton bud in water and moisten her lips to make sure her mouth did not get too dry. One afternoon, as my sister and I were chatting about the past, we looked over and saw that our mother had passed away. It was as quiet and quick as that. No fuss. Just as she would have liked it."

Thinking ahead

Not everyone will have someone who knows them "inside and out" as with Maureen and Mike. For many people, like Joan and her family, the events seem to dictate the sensible and most appropriate course of action and Joan was happy to entrust her care to her children. Nevertheless, as general awareness of dementia increases and more resources are provided, people living with dementia know that they will need additional care as their condition changes. With new advances in medicine and the significant increase in life expectancy, many are beginning to think about the care and kinds of treatment that may be offered when they reach the last stages of their life. Indeed, advance care planning as an ongoing discussion between the person and healthcare providers has become an increasingly important part of end-of-life programmes offered by the NHS.

Many people are concerned about what will happen if they lose the capacity to make decisions about their own care. Undoubtedly, using the existing legislation is a very important and helpful way forward. Therefore, in chapter 5, a solicitor explains how to make the legislation work for you.

Still, there are some other important considerations that can help to ensure the continuity of living and dying well with dementia. People with dementia may also be thinking about how they can live well with dementia when their care is entrusted to others, especially when those others are strangers or do not know them well. Thinking ahead is not simply about a list of choices or enforcing an autonomy that will cease to exist. It is about cherishing the life we have had and have now. It celebrates who we are and who and what we love.

Certainly, Christians live in the hope of fullness of life as eternal life in friendship with God. Nevertheless, this does not mean that our earthly life has little meaning or should not be lived as fully as possible. Moreover, to believe that a life is useless or burdensome fails to cherish the life we have been given. Indeed, the process of dementia is part of the gradual unfolding of the mystery of our life, and life unfolds in relationships.

In our conversations we repeatedly heard important concerns about:

- practical help and support:
- the fear of loneliness and isolation, frustrations and challenges:
- the need for:
    - ◊ useful and positive information:
    - ◊ good communication:
    - ◊ support that is tailored to people's actual situations:
    - ◊ attitudes that respect people as they are, their rich life experiences which are continuing, albeit into a more uncertain future.

Living with care: good communication and healthcare decisions

It is a part of good communication to encourage people to talk to their family and friends, to their priest or spiritual care giver, and to their doctors about how they would like to be treated in the event of a future illness, especially if there comes a time when they are no longer able to make decisions about their own care. Many people find it difficult to begin the conversation when they are fit and well, or they overreact to sensational media stories. The comments "I would not want to live like that" or "I don't want to be like that" are easy to make when we are well and in control of our lives. Yet, as many of our stories demonstrate, it is often difficult to envisage how we would cope with alterations in our health. People do change their minds as they adjust to new realities.

Conversations that are introduced gradually and gently may make it easier to discuss more specific issues as problems arise. However, much we are learning about dementia, the course of the condition is often unpredictable. For everyone, serious illness may give us time to reflect on our life and on what is important. It may also give us a new perspective on how we manage the last stages of our life. As health deteriorates and priorities change, previous wishes and desires may need to be revisited. This applies to people with and without dementia. We all need time to reflect on illness and our dying and this reflection includes consideration of our family, reconciliation and the resolution of any conflicts. Endings are a very important part of spiritual wholeness.[1]

Communicating in advance and carrying on the conversation for as long as possible is part of the process of facing up to the reality of the situation. It enables us to know what options are

[1] *A Practical Guide to the Spiritual Care of the Dying Person, 1.3.4.* Catholic Bishops' Conference of England and Wales, CTS 2010

available and what can be expected. It gives us an opportunity to sort out our affairs and prioritise what needs to be done. However, people are different. They have different pain thresholds, different resources and react differently, even to the same medication or treatment.

Good communication helps others realise what is important and what would be too burdensome for the person. Good communication can establish trust between those involved so that, should the time come when the person can no longer make their own decisions or becomes unable to communicate, that relationship of trust continues. Those entrusted with someone's care in their last days can thus be free to respond to the changing course of the illness and be guided in their decision-making.

Certainly, one of the most important and valuable things we can do for a person is to care for them in the final stages of their life.[2] However, an act of true self-giving and trust is to allow ourselves to be cared for by other people.

As part of good communication:

- talk to:
    - ◊ family, friends, professionals, doctor;
    - ◊ a minister of religion about spiritual needs.
- have conversations over a period: there is no need to rush but take time to reflect;
- be prepared to revisit your previously held views;
- ask your doctor about the likely progression of your condition and possible treatments;

[2] *A Practical Guide to the Spiritual Care of the Dying Person, 3.8.* Catholic Bishops' Conference of England and Wales, CTS 2010

- discuss your hopes, values, fears and concerns, and say what you would find too difficult to bear;
- make clear your religious commitments and wishes.

A statement of wishes:

- is not legally binding;
- may help resolve any tensions between family members and carers;
- lessen the burden of decision-making, especially when:
  - ◊ it might be stressful for families to decide;
  - ◊ where members of the family cannot agree;
  - ◊ where there are no family members;
- is not as an extension of autonomy, or a list of wishes and feelings;
- is a tool to help caregivers to make decisions that cherish a life and accept its limits;
- can express good stewardship of life and be a reflection on dying well.

A template for a statement of wishes might include:

- Should I become unable to make decisions for myself, I ask that (....names and contact details of friends/family....) be consulted about decisions made on my behalf;
- (If you have a particular religious affiliation) I also ask for a Catholic priest (Anglican minister, Rabbi, Imam…) to be contacted and to visit so that I can receive appropriate pastoral and spiritual care and (for Catholics) the sacrament of the sick during my illness and as my death approaches;
- I ask that appropriate care is given to me to preserve my life and to cure, improve, or reduce deterioration in any physical or medical condition I suffer.

A serious question in a statement of wishes concerns treatment which the individual might consider "too burdensome". There is a real danger of adding in a wish that could be interpreted as a blanket rejection of all treatments including relatively easy treatments, for example treatments that could resolve infections. Another danger is the refusal of treatment when someone is not actually dying, treatment that could be lifesaving. One suggested way of framing this is:

> I accept that death need not be resisted by all means possible. As death approaches, I ask not to be given treatment that is futile, that will not sustain me, give me comfort or relieve a condition I have. As death approaches, I ask not to be given treatment that will only briefly prolong my life and that would be overly burdensome to me or to others.

Yes, there is a level of interpretation in any statement of wishes. But that is a part of entrusting ourselves to the care of others. The point about good stewardship of our life is that we start from an option for life and we think carefully about decision-making: decisions are not made on the worthwhileness of life but on the appropriateness of treatment for this particular person in this particular circumstance. Every life is precious from its very beginning to its natural end.

Accompaniment towards the end

Co-ordinated care

For most people a stay in hospital is unnerving and difficult, regardless of a diagnosis of dementia or someone's confusion and fear.

People living with dementia often make difficult patients simply because they are out of their normal routine in an unfamiliar place with unfamiliar people and they may feel frustrated if their normal routine is disrupted for instance if they like to walk about. However, sometimes they do have to be admitted to hospital and many find the professionalism and resources of hospital care reassuring. Pre-covid, statistics for all groups showed that although most wanted to die at home, with the proper support, most people died in hospital.[3] If we remember that long before end-of-life care is needed, routine care has been already put in place, then there may be more timely moments for discussing with professionals how and where future care can be given. This can reveal other options.

Many families want to look after their loved one at home until the end of their life. As Maureen and Mike's story shows, this is possible with co-ordinated care from GPs, other healthcare professionals, specialist teams and others who can provide appropriate support. Joan's story shows that care homes also can provide good and appropriate support.

As the person approaches the end of life, good palliative care is vital. Some innovative work links hospice support to that in the community and in people's own homes. Some hospices have already published guides to support dementia care at home where professionals, carers and the person living with dementia can all work together.[4] While many hospices are not yet engaged

[3] *What's Important to Me: a review of choice in end of life care*. gov.uk (2015) 75% of people wished to die at home with the proper support (p.3). However, the report notes that in 2013 in England 48% of people died in hospital, 21% in care homes, 5% in hospices and 22% died at home (pp.16-17).

[4] See for instance http://hopeforhome.org.uk/projects/hospiceuk/; https://professionals.hospiceuk.org/what-we-offer/clinical-and-care-support/hospice-enabled-dementia-care

in such set-ups, there is a real incentive among those delivering care to see hospice-based expertise and experience become more and more dementia-friendly.

Hospices:

- are concerned with:
  - ◊ dying, death and bereavement;
  - ◊ living with these realities;
- seek to help people find coping strategies in challenging situations;
- have experience of supporting family and informal carers;
- have expertise in recognising when people are dying;
- provide appropriate relief from distressing symptoms.

The Gold Standards Framework

If you are involved with a care or nursing home, you may be aware of the Gold Standards Framework. The Gold Standards Framework was developed in 2000 from professional expertise in primary care and was introduced into care homes in 2004. It is now the biggest palliative care initiative in care homes in the UK.

The framework has three steps:

- to identify the stage and condition of patients who are in their last year of life;
- to assess their current and future clinical and personal needs;
- to work out a treatment and care plan.

The key tasks in this planning are to:

- ensure good communication with the person, their family and carers, and professional;

- have coordinated care;
- control symptoms;
- offer care support;
- develop a personalised care of the dying pathway;
- encourage continuing learning and reflection;
- put into practice listening to people and their families;
- provide patients with high quality care that is aligned with their preferences;
- anticipate needs through careful pre-planning;
- improve the confidence of professionals and care home staff through encouraging teamwork;
- aim at more home-based and less hospital-based care.

In 2020, Hospice UK, the national charity for hospice and end-of-life care, joined forces with the Gold Standards Framework Centre, an organisation that provides training in end-of-life care. This was in order to improve the quality of care in all different kinds of settings, from the homes, hospitals, care homes and retirement villages, to prisons.[5]

There is now an additional focus on caring for people living with dementia in the last years of their lives. This involves training professionals and carers in improving awareness of dementia, notably in using life stories to build up a personal picture of the person; developing better and more appropriate tools for assessing pain and distress; improving communication; reducing hospital admissions, and enabling more people to live and die at home.

[5] https://www.goldstandardsframework.org.uk/

Better awareness of dementia is not only about the different types of dementia nor is it simply awareness of the way in which dementia progresses in an individual. Better awareness indicates that some confusions and behaviours may be explained by easily remedied conditions such as pain, constipation, infection or even boredom or fear of unfamiliar places and people.

Better awareness reminds us that improved access to information, advice and support groups, and developing dementia-friendly communities are vital for people living with dementia, their families and carers. Significantly, better awareness reminds us that all people have the same need for good care in all the areas of life – physical, emotional, mental and spiritual – and that all people have a dignity that cannot be lost even if to some individuals, they might seem to be in undignified situations.

Accompanying

People accompanying a person towards the end of life may be faced with several issues that the person themselves may have difficulty in articulating. Often it is a family member or carer, rather than the person living with dementia, who needs additional support.

There is the obvious question of medical uncertainty. Treatment decisions, especially decisions to withdraw treatment, should be based on an accurate diagnosis of the cause of deterioration, which clinicians should be ready to re-assess regularly.

Family members and carers are not usually professional clinicians. As Maureen's experience illustrates, there were times when she was not sure what was happening to Mike, and she was anxious about how things would eventually work out.

- Check that the person is getting the information they need, and that the information is understandable.
- Ask if they want to discuss anything further or have worries about what is going to happen.

The person who is dying may show signs of physical or psychological distress. First and foremost, clinical staff have a professional responsibility to their patient.

- If possible, ask how they are coping and if there is anything you can do to make them more comfortable.
- Make sure symptoms are assessed and managed and revisit this frequently in case there are any changes. Involve professional help. This may include a priest or chaplain to help with spiritual distress (spiritual assessments will be discussed in chapter 6).
- Ask how family members and carers are managing and if they need more support.

If this is still possible and appropriate:

- involve the person living with dementia in any decision-making and to do this, think about treating delirium or avoiding sedation;
- show a continued interest in somebody's life and interests; continue to talk to them even if there is no response;
- encourage participation in activities such as choice of music or prayers.

Feeding people

As Joan's story shows, families and carers are rightly concerned when their loved one stops eating and drinking. In Joan's case, she was drifting in and out of consciousness and it was obvious that the end was near. However, sometimes it is difficult to know how close the person is to death.

In the end stages of dementia, it seems that the person's intake of food and fluids (nutrition and hydration), naturally decrease and there are often increasing problems with swallowing.

It is important to try to keep someone eating and drinking even in small amounts, but when a person has difficulties with these then, understandably, their family and carers may be worried that their loved one is starving to death or dehydrating.

There are ways of providing food and fluids that bypass the need for oral help with feeding.

- Tube feeding:
  - ◊ via a nasogastric tube: a tube is passed through the nose and into the stomach;
  - ◊ directly through a surgical hole in the stomach wall (PEG feeding);
- drip feeding of fluids:
  - ◊ directly into a vein;
  - ◊ just under the skin.

However, these interventions usually require hospital admission, and the person may find the experience of tubes so distressing that they pull out their tubes.

Making a judgement about switching from oral to tube feeding (clinically assisted nutrition and hydration) requires a careful discernment of the risks, burdens and benefits as well as a determination on how close the person is to death.

When we think about treatment and withdrawing treatment, it helps if we remember that we both recognise the limits of earthly life and do not aim at hastening death. Under the Mental Capacity Act nutrition and hydration provided artificially is considered to be medical treatment. However, food and fluids do not have the same human and ethical status as other medical interventions. Nevertheless, research seems to show that the person adjusts to their body slowing down and this means that the person no longer wants to eat and drink, and no longer feels hungry and thirsty.

Giving food and water, even by tube, is a natural means of preserving life. This is not only basic care, but it also represents a profound act of solidarity and care.

The next steps for Maureen

The end of life often leaves us in a kind of limbo. Our next chapter is a very practical one and it looks at how people can make the legislation work for them as they approach the end of life. Following this, in chapter 6, we look at spirituality for people living with dementia and we include here further reflection on the end of life.

Reflection for the reader:

What do you want at the end of your life?
Have you told anyone?

Chapter 5

Making the legislation work for you

By Lucy Marie Antonia Cortis (Solicitor)

Advanced Care Planning is, put simply, a method by which the person can make decisions about the future care he/she would wish to receive if he/she were to lose the mental capacity to make such decisions for themselves. While the term Advanced Care Planning is usually focused on someone's medical needs, it is important not to forget the potential financial implications, for both the person concerned and the family, caused by a loss of mental capacity, especially if it were to occur suddenly.

From a purely healthcare view point the advantages of Advanced Care Planning were highlighted during a recent review of patients with both dementia and other forms of cognitive impairments.[1] These advantages included the implementation

[1] Robinson L, Dickinson C, Rousseau N, Beyer F, Clark A, Hughes J, *et al.* "A systematic review of the effectiveness of advanced care planning interventions for people with cognitive impairment and dementia". *Age Ageing* 2012; 41: 263-9

of less aggressive medical intervention and perhaps most importantly, a better quality of life towards the end. While this was admittedly a relatively small study, its conclusions are often mirrored by my own practical experience in which many clients who have activated such plans have ultimately received treatments which more accurately accord with their personal wishes and views, thereby allowing the end of their lives to be both dignified and peaceful.

Admittedly Advanced Care Planning is often complicated by the vast array of documents available and in many cases the terminology used. In this chapter, I have therefore attempted to provide a useful guide to the options available as well as de-coding some of the more commonly used words and phrases thereby allowing you to formulate a plan which works for both you and your family.

Section 1: The assessment of Mental Capacity

What exactly is meant by the term Mental Capacity?

In plain English, the term Mental Capacity simply means a person's ability to make their own decisions. An individual will be treated as having Mental Capacity if he/she can:

(i) understand the information relevant to the decision to be made;

(ii) retain the information (even if only over a relatively short period);

(iii) utilise the above-mentioned information during the decision-making process and;

(iv) communicate that decision to other through any available means.

It is, however, important to guard against overcomplicating the information which is relevant for a specific decision to be made. As Baker J cited in his judgement in CC v KK & STCC [2012] EWHC 2136 (COP)[2], it is not necessary for a person to demonstrate a capacity to understand and weigh up every detail of the respective options, but merely the salient factors.

The assessment of an individual's capacity is also decision-specific. Therefore, just because an individual may not have the capacity to consent to a specific medical treatment does not necessarily mean that they lack the capacity to decide on their own daily routine, for example.

The law surrounding the determination of Mental Capacity is contained in Mental Capacity Act 2005. This act is composed of five key principles which govern the way in which decisions can be made on behalf of people who are deemed to no longer possess sufficient Mental Capacity to make certain decisions for themselves. A discussion of each principle follows.

Principle 1: A presumption of capacity

The basic principle is that every adult is presumed to have the capacity to make their own decisions (regardless of their medical condition or disability) unless it can be proved that they do not. Therefore, a diagnosis of dementia, for example, does not automatically mean that the individual has lost Mental Capacity.

[2] The reference is to a court case: in sensitive cases the full name is not given hence CC and KK. EWHC is the common abbreviation for the England and Wales High Court.

Principle 2: Individuals being supported to make their own decisions

Before a person can be deemed to lack the capacity to make a specific decision for themselves, they must have been assisted, in every practicable way, to make it for themselves. This may be by presenting the information to them in a different format, asking them at different times of the day or by involving other family members in the decision. Even if a person's lack of capacity can be demonstrated, it is still vitally important that they are involved in the decision-making process.

Principle 3: Unwise decisions

We all have the right to make an unwise or otherwise eccentric decision and this, on its own, is not a reason for treating someone as having lost capacity.

Principle 4: Best interests

Any decisions made or actions taken on behalf of someone who is deemed to have lost capacity must always be taken in their best interest.

Principle 5: Less restrictive options

Before any action can be taken on behalf of someone who has lost capacity, it is important to consider whether the same action could be taken in a different way which would be less restrictive to their individual rights and freedoms.

As many loved ones of those living with dementia will be aware, the loss of capacity is not a "bright line" with the person suddenly (at the time of diagnosis) becoming incapable of making their own decisions. Capacity can fluctuate over time – even within the same day – and therefore its assessment must be both time and decision-specific.

How is Mental Capacity assessed?

The assessment of Mental Capacity is a two-stage process. First it is necessary to determine whether there is "an impairment of or disturbance in the functioning of a person's mind or brain" and then, if the answer is yes, is this impairment/ disturbance sufficient that the person lacks the capacity to make a particular decision?

As part of the process, an individual will be assessed on their ability to understand the information provided and also, whether they can retain it long enough to reach an informed decision (bearing in mind Principle 2 above).

Section 2: The documents

Advanced Statements

These are statements outlining a person's wishes for their future such as, their goals for care or, their personal values. While such statements are not, in and of themselves, legally binding they can provide vital evidence of a person's wishes when a "best interests" decision is being taken on their behalf. Also, while it is possible to make a verbal Advanced Statement, it is often more practical for them to be in writing.

Examples of statements which people may include are:

- I would wish to remain in my own home for as long as possible;
- If I had to move into a care home, I would want to bring my photographs and music with me;
- I would like to continue having a glass of wine with my evening meal.

The wish to remain in one's own home is widely held. However, even if such a desire is contained within your Advanced Statement (either orally or in writing) it may have to be disregarded if it is no longer in the person's best interests to remain there.

Advanced Decision to refuse treatment:

In comparison to the above, an Advanced Decision is legally binding. Such a decision can be made orally. But if it involves the refusal of life-sustaining treatment, such as cardio-pulmonary resuscitation (CPR), then it must be in writing, signed by the individual in the presence of a witness, who should then also sign the document. The Advanced Decision should also clearly state that the individual is fully aware that in refusing such treatment they may die.

While a person is free to refuse any type of treatment which does not accord with the person's beliefs or wishes, a person cannot refuse basic care. The term "basic care" encompasses things such as repositioning on the bed or offers of food and drink by mouth.

While it is helpful for Advanced Decisions to be as specific as possible, it is important to note that if the circumstances referred to within the decision do not apply to one's current circumstances, then, it may not be followed by medical professionals.

An example of this is a refusal for antibiotics to be applied to treat a chest infection may not be applied to the treatment of a urinary tract infection (if it is deemed to be in the person's best interests). Such decisions may not be valid if the circumstances have materially changed (for example, an unanticipated advance in medical science) since the Advanced Decision was made and, there are reasons to believe that, had the person been aware of these changes, then they may have reached a different conclusion.

Whilst there is no specified time limit on such decisions, it is (especially in light of the above) important that they are reviewed every few years (whilst one retains capacity) to ensure that they are still in accordance with one's wishes.

What is a Power of Attorney?

Powers of Attorney are legal documents through which one can nominate the person (or persons) whom one trusts to make decisions on his/her behalf if, in the future, that person were to become unable to make such decisions for him/herself.

There are different types of Powers of Attorney which, are discussed in more detail below.

General Powers of Attorney

A General Power of Attorney automatically comes to an end once the person making the power has lost capacity.

Lasting Powers of Attorney (LPAs)

The importance of LPAs was recently highlighted by the organisation *Solicitors for the Elderly* that found that 99% of respondents were leaving decisions about their future health and welfare to chance, with a further 41% admitting that they had made no provisions for later life including a will, Pension Plan or LPAs.

LPAs replaced the old Enduring Powers of Attorney (EPAs) which could only authorise an attorney (person(s) nominated in the document) to make financial decisions on one's behalf. There was no power under an EPA for an Attorney to make any decision relating to health and/or personal welfare. Whilst it is now no longer possible to create a new EPA, any such documents which were in existence prior to the cut-off date of 1 October 2007 will continue to be valid. Whilst such documents did not need to be registered upon their creation, they are now required to be registered as soon as legally formulated and most certainly before someone is deemed to have lost, or to be losing, mental capacity.

There are two different types of LPAs: Property and Financial Affairs, and Health and Welfare. To be legally valid both LPAs need to be registered with the Office of the Public Guardian (OPG) before they can be used by a person's Attorneys.

Property and Financial Affairs

The Property and Financial Affairs LPA can be used as soon as it is registered. However, whilst someone still retains mental capacity, the Attorneys can only act with that person's consent.

The decisions that the Attorneys will be able to make on one's behalf under such a document include running somebody's bank accounts and any other investments, making decisions about investing in or selling investments, selling property and spending one's money.

Attorneys can only make gifts in favour of another:

- on limited occasions such as birthdays and Christmas;
- provided they are given in the same way as the person always done;
- provided that the amounts given or spent are reasonable when compared to the person's total assets.

Any other gifts cannot be made without the authority of the OPG. This means that extreme care is required if the Attorney is the primary financial provider for another family member.

Health and Welfare

Under a Health and Welfare LPA, the Attorneys can only make decisions on someone's behalf once they have been shown to lack the mental capacity to make such decisions and, the LPA has been registered with the OPG. The registration process can often take up to ten weeks to finalise.

The Attorneys can make the following types of decision:

- the care facility of residence;
- day-to-day issues like dress, diet and daily routine;
- giving or refusing consent to certain types of health care including life-sustaining treatment.

Life-sustaining treatment

Life-sustaining treatments means any treatment which a doctor considers necessary to keep one alive such as:

- a serious surgical operation such as a heart bypass;
- receiving chemotherapy, radiotherapy or other forms of cancer treatment;
- an organ transplant;
- artificial nutrition or hydration.

However, if one develops pneumonia a simple course of antibiotics could be considered life-sustaining.

A carer cannot refuse someone basic care such as offering food, water, etc – even if the person refuses to take it – and therefore is required to continue to offer it. However, the Attorney can refuse consent for an invasive procedure such as PEG insertion (a feeding tube inserted directly into the stomach). The Attorney cannot consent to euthanasia, neither can the donor (person formulating the LPA).

The Attorneys cannot make decisions about life-sustaining treatment unless they have received specific authority within the terms of an LPA. Even with this authority, such decisions will still be made in consultation with a medical professional.

Through my practice, I have noted that there appear to be several popular misconceptions relating to Health and Welfare decisions and I have therefore tried to address a few of the more common ones below.

Will my doctor not just discuss things with my family anyway?

Whilst doctors must always act in what they consider to be the patient's best interests, these actions may not always be in accordance with the person's wishes. For example, whilst most doctors will consult with a patient's family if the patient lacks capacity to make such decisions themselves legally, this is a relatively grey area. If there is no LPA for Health and Welfare and the doctor decides that it is in an individual's best interests to maintain confidentiality, the family may not therefore be consulted regarding care plans, thus making an already distressing situation that much more difficult for them.

The next of kin myth

Whereas in a healthcare setting the term "next of kin" is often used to identify the person with whom medics can communicate, the term has no status in law whilst someone is alive. This means that without the legal authority to do so (granted through one of the documents referred to in this section) they have no authority to act on their behalf regarding financial or healthcare decisions. In some cases, the next of kin is not the person whom the individual would wish to make such decisions on perhaps because their actual next of kin is frail and likely to become unduly anxious, or perhaps because they live at a distance and a quick decision is required for the person's immediate wellbeing.

The sad case of Betty Figg

Nothing highlights the importance of such documents as the case of 86-year-old Betty Figg who had dementia.

Mrs Figg's case was widely reported in the press at the time. She did not have a Health and Welfare LPA and, after a stay in hospital, Adult Social Services became involved in her care and recommended that she be placed in a care home. Initially her family agreed with this. However, after becoming concerned about the level of care her mother was receiving, Mrs Figg's daughter brought her mother to live with her. These actions then prompted Social Services to obtain a warrant to forcibly return Mrs Figg to the care home where she remained for a further two months. In the meantime, her daughter attended a two-day course and made renovations to her home in order to convince Social Services that the environment was suitable for her to care for her mother.

Whilst the case of Betty Figg is admittedly an extreme example, it is worth noting that this whole situation could have been avoided. Had a Health and Welfare LPA been in place, there would have been no need for doctors to involve Social Services and the Attorney would have been able to make the decisions instead.

What else can my Health and Welfare LPA be used for?

Health and Welfare LPAs are more often used to assist with more routine decisions surrounding a patient's life such as their day-to-day life, daily routine or even who is allowed to visit. Whilst such decisions may appear to be relatively minor, they can have a huge impact upon the overall quality of a person's life.

Another important fact surrounding LPAs of this type is its use in making decisions regarding life-sustaining treatment. The 2018 Supreme Court decision in A NHS Trust *v* Y dealt with a man in his fifties who suffered a cardiac arrest. This caused his brain to be deprived of oxygen resulting in permanent damage and rendering him comatose. Whilst Mr Y did not have an LPA for Health and Welfare, his family believed that he would not have wanted his life to be artificially extended and the doctors agreed that this was not in his best interest. However, the hospital trust sought a declaration from the court that no criminal liability would result from the removal of his artificial feeding tube as this would ultimately result in Mr Y's death.

In her judgement Lady Black acknowledged that whilst the Mental Capacity Act 2005 did make provision for the court to make decisions about an individual's personal welfare where necessary, it did not single out a specific sub-class of decisions where such applications were always necessary. However, if a family and the medics disagree regarding potential care and there is no LPA of this type in place, the necessary court hearing will thereby place more strain on the family during what is already an extremely difficult time.

By far the most common type of LPA is the Property and Financial Affairs power. Due to recent changes in the practices of many local authorities and NHS trusts, they are becoming increasingly more important.

The Attorneys

The Attorney is the person who one has personally selected to assist one with the decisions noted below.

It is best practice to have more than one Attorney in case one of them should die or be incapacitated themselves. The

Attorneys can be appointed to act "jointly" which means that they must always act together, or they can be appointed "jointly and severally" which means that they can act together or independently. This may be useful if, for example, one of them dies or themselves becomes incapable of continuing to deal with one's affairs or is away on holiday. It means that the other can continue to act and make the appropriate decisions on one's behalf.

Alternatively, one can appoint a Replacement Attorney who will only act if, for any reason, the original Attorney is permanently unable to fulfil this role. The Attorneys (both original and replacement) must abide by the principles of the Mental Capacity Act Code of Practice and must make decisions in one's best interests, including consideration of one's known wishes and beliefs.

Can I include any restriction, condition or guidance for my Attorneys?

If one does not include any restrictions or conditions within one's LPA, the Attorneys will be able to make **all** decisions about one's health and welfare or financial affairs (as appropriate) on one's behalf.

One can include conditions detailing procedures they **must** follow such as:

- not consenting to treatment involving blood products;
- instruction on advice they **must** seek, such as consulting a particular solicitor or financial advisor.

Please note in relation to the Health and Welfare LPA a restriction relating to the *type* of treatment options one should or should not receive may become invalid if the treatment options have materially changed since one lost competence.

- Any advanced refusal of medical treatment must be specific to the circumstances as they have arisen.
- Any refusal of treatment which is not applicable to the circumstances may not be followed.
- Doctors cannot be obliged to provide treatment which, in their medical opinion, is clinically inappropriate or which has a very small chance of success.

Who else needs to be involved?

When one enters into an LPA, a "certificate provider" acts as an independent judge of mental capacity.

Whilst not an exhaustive list the following individuals would not be classed as independent e.g: one of your attorneys or a relative, or a business partner / employee of your attorney. For further information please see the Office of Public Guidance website: https://www.gov.uk/government/publications/make-a-lasting-power-of-attorney/lp12-make-and-register-your-lasting-power-of-attorney-a-guide-web-version

A certificate provider

- must sign the document for its registration;
- confirms:

◊ that they are satisfied that the document and its purpose are understood by the person on whose behalf the LPA is needed;
◊ that there has been no undue pressure to enter into the LPA.

Ending an LPA

One can terminate the LPAs at any time so long as one retains Mental Capacity to make the decision.

An LPA is automatically ended following one's death or the death (or loss of capacity) of the Attorney (if a Replacement Attorney has not been appointed). For this reason, it is often common practice to appoint more than one Attorney or, to ensure that a Replacement Attorney is named within the document. The LPA will also be automatically terminated if one has named one's spouse as an Attorney if subsequently divorced.

Deputyships

If, however, an individual no longer has the Mental Capacity necessary to create the above-mentioned documents then, an application to the Court of Protection will become necessary. The court will then appoint someone to make such decisions in the individual's best interests.

There are, however, several key differences between an LPA and a Deputyship which need to be considered.

Under an LPA:

- one can chose who one would like to make such decisions if one is unable to do so;
- it is cheaper and less time-consuming;
- there is no annual supervision fee and insurance.

Under a Deputyship:

- the Deputy is appointed by the Court of Protection and may therefore not be the one whom the person concerned would have specifically chosen;
- it takes longer to process and can cause issues for families, especially if there are urgent bills which need to be paid and they are unable to access accounts;
- it requires the payment of an annual supervision fee and insurance, although these can usually be reclaimed from one's funds once the Deputyship is granted;
- it requires the provision to the Court of an Annual Return; this report provides information regarding the decisions which have been made on one's behalf during the year as well as providing summary accounts for the court to approve.

Whilst it is possible to appoint an Attorney to deal with one's Health and Welfare decisions (as outlined above), Health and Welfare deputyships are rare. One of the main reasons for this is due to the difficulty of appointing someone to make medical decisions on behalf of an individual without any indication of what their wishes would have been.

Whilst each case regarding a personal welfare Deputy is decided on its own merits, their appointment may be required in the following circumstances.

- If a series of linked welfare decisions need to be made on someone's behalf, it may not be practicable for each individual decision to be brought to the attention of the court.
- The court accepts that to make such an appointment would be in one's best interest.
- There is a breakdown in trust and confidence between one's family and the healthcare professionals regarding one's ongoing care.

Whilst these issues are very personal and sensitive, it is important that they are carefully considered in order to avoid doubts, regrets and misunderstandings but acted upon in a timely manner.

Chapter 6

Practical spirituality

"It is only with the heart that one can see rightly; what is essential is invisible to the eye."[1]

Spirituality is essential to every person, although it is often invisible. It goes beyond the tangible aspects of daily life to promote a deeper awareness and understanding of a perceived meaning of life itself. All human beings are spiritual whether or not they belong to a particular religious tradition or consider themselves to be religious.

Spirituality has both invisible and visible aspects insofar as what is internally perceived can be borne out in observable practice.

Spirituality's invisible aspect can be described as an "inner life" that is uniquely human, personal and soul-touching. It has two aspects:

[1] Antoine de Saint-Exupéry, Egmont, 2001 *The Little Prince.*

- relating to intangible needs and appreciation, such as relationships, music, art, poetry, beauty, joy that is inspired by creation and the world around us;
- relating to religious and moral belief and practice, such as daily prayer, reading scriptures or holy writings, reception of the sacraments, attending religious services and works of charity.

Fostering and encouraging this first characteristic of the inner life is a vital part of living fully with dementia. The second facet of the inner life, spirituality, concerns someone's relationship with God.

Whether or not someone is religious, there is a relationship with God – even saying that God does not exist is a statement about a particular personal relationship with, and attitude towards, God.

The invisible inner life of spirituality is often described as the way in which someone finds meaning and connection or finds sources of hope in the world.

If we think of spirituality only in terms of finding meaning, then it is all too easy to make the mistake of thinking that the person in the last stages of living with dementia is no longer spiritual, especially if they appear distanced from their former inner human life of enjoying activities in the world. However, once we realise that spirituality is as much, if not more, to do with God than our own abilities, then we can understand how it is that every human being, no matter their situation, is a spiritual being.

Visible and invisible spirituality in the parish and faith community

A person's visible spirituality is often expressed in their interaction with their faith community. In the early stages of dementia keeping to the same routine of the person is important:

- attending the same church services;
- sitting in the same area of the church;
- continuing with regular activities, such as arranging flowers, working as a catechist, perhaps with extra support, for as long as possible.

A dementia-friendly parish can:

- allocate a responsible parishioner to look out for the person living with dementia, especially if unaccompanied;
- deal with potentially awkward situations in a sensitive and caring way;
- enable someone to continue with regular activities for as long as possible by offering support when it's needed;
- show awareness of both the condition of dementia and a recognition of people who may need support through:
    - ◊ regular dementia awareness meetings;
    - ◊ making dementia the concern of the whole parish;
    - ◊ reassuring the person and their family that he/she still belongs to that faith community;
    - ◊ highlighting the responsibility of clergy to raise their own awareness about the different types of dementia;
    - ◊ sensitivity regarding the importance of their confidentiality, consent and safeguarding;
- establish appropriate safeguarding policies:

- designated accompaniers should:
  - ◊ have proper safeguarding checks;
  - ◊ remember that they are dealing with vulnerable people;
  - ◊ recognise that some people may not want others to know of their diagnosis;
  - ◊ offer discreet support with the consent of the person and their loved ones.

The hope is that people will begin to feel more comfortable relying on the support of others and be more trusting once dementia becomes everyone's concern. At all stages of accompaniment, the importance of maintaining human dignity is paramount, even if at times it seems challenging and difficult to implement. This key principle of Catholic social teaching and common to all faith groups, should be both the starting point and the goal of care.

Reflect on your parish or community experience

- How dementia-aware is your community? Have you got the relevant safeguarding policies in place?
- What is your experience of identifying and supporting a person with dementia and or their loved ones?

Practising faith

Faith can be lived out in many ways. However, for many religious people, attending church is a vital and necessary part of how they practise their faith. Churches are in a unique position because they can often reach people who are otherwise on the margins, offering a ready-made community and fellowship and, most of all, hope. Even when a person can no longer attend church, with enough support, they can still feel a part of the community. Moreover, ensuring that the Gospel message is accessible to all is an integral aspect of church ministry.

Church communities can support people with dementia and their families in a myriad of ways:

- being a welcoming ccommunity;
- giving people lifts to and from services;
- producing large-print service sheets;
- arranging home visits and organising events.

We heard Maggie's story in chapter 1. Maggie was very involved in her church, especially the Mothers Prayers group. As things gradually became more challenging for Maggie, her friends wanted to help her, but it was difficult to know how to do this. It is all too easy to assume that we know what help a person needs. On the one hand church communities need to offer their help in an open-handed manner, ready to do what is needed and not make assumptions. We also need people to tell their stories and to explain what they would like. Undoubtedly, the stigma associated with dementia makes any disclosure difficult. But we must start somewhere and, as all our stories have shown, the generosity of people who are willing to share their stories will build up better communities. What is important is for people to know that the community is ready to help.

Practicalities: access and environment

Being a welcoming community starts quite simply with access:

- parking spaces, level ground, well-defined paths and clear signage;
- a welcomer who can offer practical assistance;

- quiet space for people who may:
    - ◊ feel overwhelmed;
    - ◊ need extra space;
    - ◊ time to get settled;
- good lighting and sound systems with hearing loops;
- adequate toilet facilities;
- comfortable seating;
- comfortably warm building;
- space should a person need to walk around.

Reflection

In a parish group, walk around your building inside and out.

- What barriers may there be for people with reduced mobility or perception difficulties?
- Is it easy for them to navigate their route?

Everyone can contribute

There often comes a point in time when engaging with parish life is no longer possible for someone living with dementia. Ideally, accompaniers will already know them and their family as this is crucial to establishing a healthy relationship. This connection will enable the accompanier to know the person's favourite prayers, hymns, devotions and saints. Nevertheless, what may be challenging, but needs to be addressed in a sensitive way, could be if the family's praying practices are not strong and they do not seem to understand that this aspect of life is still important to the person living with dementia.

This leads us into the more invisible aspects of spirituality. What seems to be clear is that, despite seeming to "withdraw" into another place in their minds, many people living with dementia are still able to pray and their spiritual lives are still present. Hence, we must presume nothing about what the person can and cannot spiritually appreciate.

Moreover, we can never underestimate the power of Our Lord to bring comfort to people in any situation or the value that frequent, reverent words have for people with dementia, and their families and carers.

Caring for someone's spirituality has long been seen as part of good care – and this includes supporting families and carers. Good care is person-centred. It is tailored to the needs of the individual and can help everyone to rediscover hope and to maintain their resilience and inner strength. But to work out what care the person needs we require some form of assessment of their spiritual needs, including the role of faith and prayers in their life.

Assessing spiritual needs

Spirituality can be a great source of support and comfort for people. This applies, not only to the person living with dementia, but also to their family, friends and supporters.

Spirituality:

- can help people cope by giving meaning to challenging situations;
- helps people adjust to the new reality following a dementia diagnosis;
- offers support in rediscovering hope;
- encourages resilience and inner strength in difficult times;

- connects people;
- can address spiritual distress.

There are some useful spiritual tools that can be adapted and used to aid in planning good care for people with dementia. These tools, when appropriately used:

- employ a simple assessment to find out what matters to a person;
- vary in complexity and flexibility;
- can be utilised in conjunction with the tool we explored in chapter 2
- facilitate talking about what matters;
- are not a series of questions so much as a focus for opening a conversation;
- can create a more trusting and friendly relationship with the person where:
    - ◊ they can feel heard and supported;
    - ◊ their spirituality is shared and appreciated;
    - ◊ they identify avenues for spiritual care and assistance;
- enable a relationship to become more truly human.

First, we can identify a basic spirituality tool that simply gathers essential information. If someone is already involved in parish life or in another faith-based community life then their faith affiliation will be clear. There may be situations, for instance, when a person is new to a care home, when this is less obvious. However, as this tool provides quite a static view of the person's spiritual life, it is useful to establish a deeper spiritual history.

The tool determines:

- faith affiliation;
- religious or cultural needs regarding:
    - ◊ diet;
    - ◊ religious observances;
    - ◊ restrictions, for instance, on treatment with blood products.

Spiritual history

A spiritual history:

- links spiritual, religious and cultural life and care;
- acknowledges personal history;
- enhances care planning through:
    - ◊ dialogue with individual and significant others, including family and carers;
    - ◊ identification of available resources;
- recognises changing needs regarding:
    - ◊ circumstances;
    - ◊ relationships;
- is not about:
    - ◊ faith content;
    - ◊ judging or "fixing" belief;
- recognises how faith and beliefs help with coping;
- respects faith and beliefs even if different from those of the assessor.

A variety of spiritual history tools available to healthcare professionals and hospital chaplains can be adapted for use outside of a hospital setting.

Successful spiritual histories and assessments tend to be brief and easy to remember, usually by creating a memorable acronym formulated to obtain the relevant information. They can be used creatively rather than simply as formulae to gather information. An easy set of letter prompts for the assessor allows for flexibility and for slotting the assessment into a conversation.

Five of the most common spiritual assessment tools are **HOPE, FICA, FAITH, SPIRIT** and **FACT.** Each is slightly different and one may be more appropriate than another depending on the situation of the person with dementia, but they all try to do similar things. They combine the basic spirituality tool with a deeper conversation about spirituality.

H hope – personal sources of hope, meaning and connection

O organisations – belonging to an organised religion or belief system

P personal – personal spirituality or belief practices

E effect – effect on care, for instance in terms of dietary requirements, assistance from a chaplain or how someone faces dementia

F faith and belief – do they help?

I importance of these beliefs – how important are they?

C community support – is support needed from a religious or other community?

A address in care – how do we address all of these issues once we have identified them – faith and belief, importance of belief, community support – in the care and support we are giving?

F faith and or spiritual beliefs – identified religious faith or spiritual beliefs

A application – application of religious beliefs to health

I involved and importance – involvement in a faith community and its importance

T treatment – impact of spiritual views on treatment

H help – required help with spiritual concerns

S spiritual belief system – identified religious faith or spiritual beliefs

P personal spirituality – beliefs and practices

- which are very important
- which are less important
- personal perceived importance of religion and spirituality

I integration with a spiritual community – membership of a particular group

- active participation
- extent of participation
- available support

R ritualised practices and restrictions –

- observed practices
- forbidden or discouraged practices
- extent of observance

I implications for care – aspects of religious belief and practice to be kept in mind during care planning and implementation

T terminal care planning – how do your beliefs influence your views on your care?

F faith or beliefs – what gives life meaning and purpose?

A active –

- involvement in faith and faith community
- available faith support
- access to faith needs

C coping, comfort, conflicts and concerns –

- perceived levels of coping
- faith as comfort
- presence of beliefs-care conflict
- concerns

T treatment plan – this point of the assessment is not about obtaining information. Rather it is a judgment on where there may be basic needs, gaps or additional needs that must be addressed.

The advantage of going more deeply into a person's spiritual history is that it gives the opportunity to identify if there are any questions the person has, and it allows for the possibility of remedying any misconceptions. For instance, some Christians may be worried that they must always have treatment no matter what, or that they cannot refuse burdensome and futile treatment, or that their illnesses are a punishment from God.

These spiritual history tools were not formulated specifically with the person living with dementia in mind and may well be more effective in the early stages of dementia. Nevertheless, they can be used to build up a good holistic picture of the person – after all spirituality is an aspect of every human being. Discussing foods, celebrations, music, important times of the year and handling objects like rosary beads, prayer books, Christmas decorations or wooden eggs may spark something of the spiritual in the conversation.

We must be aware that some objects may produce an unexpected response. When Rose was in hospital her daughter, Mary, brought in her mother's rosary but this caused Rose considerable distress and she kept pushing it away. When Mary spoke to the chaplain, the chaplain suggested that Rose may have thought that this meant that she was dying.

Reflection for the reader:

What do you think of these different tools?

Do you think that there are any major differences between them?

Would you find them helpful?

Image of God

In conversations with people, a good starting point is often a discussion about somebody's image of God. This can tell us a lot about how the person faces up to their new reality as they live with dementia. For instance, a view of God as a supreme judge may inspire worry about things that they have done or failed to do in the past, possibly causing considerable distress.

Someone who has not thought about God except in terms of an impersonal being or an abstract figure, may find it difficult to relate to an image of God as a loving and forgiving father. For the victim of previous poor or abusive relationships, the idea of God as Father may trigger serious distress – even saying the Our Father may present real difficulty.

Reflection for the reader:

What is your image of God?

Has it changed?

Spirituality

Spirituality is a uniquely personal grace from God and we should be careful not to impose a particular way of doing things on others. Not everyone finds comfort in saying the Rosary and not everyone says regular prayers. People change and many people find new ways of deepening their spirituality. However, we should also be sensitive and careful not to challenge a person's beliefs when such questioning would cause them harm or a crisis in faith.

Anyone who accompanies someone in their faith journey should be aware of their own limitations and be ready, with the consent of the person they are accompanying, to refer to someone with greater expertise.

Everybody, including those who accompany others, is at a different stage in their faith and spiritual journey. It is often enough simply to remind someone that they are remembered by God.

Practical spirituality

Our senses can take us out of ourselves and into a beautiful world that we can all share. God created the world and endowed it with a sacred beauty before gifting it to us.

As we saw in our Chapter 3 on living well with dementia, a multi-sensory approach can really enhance a person's quality of life especially as they increasingly rely on their feelings and emotions. Moreover, our most profound memories are often associated with our senses and a touch, taste, smell, hearing or sight can take us back in time and place, and to people.

Although spirituality is related to the inner life, signs, symbols and the senses all have a part to play in fostering the spiritual. Human beings are a profound unity of the material and the spiritual. It is no coincidence, therefore, that the Christian sacraments use tangible materials – water, oil, bread and wine – to express the invisible and spiritual.

Both music and silence are associated spirituality's visible aspects of religious and devotional practice. Words related to singing and song thread their way throughout the Christian Bible. Music and song help us to express what is often beyond the ability of words to communicate.

A person with later stage dementia can still respond to a favourite hymn and even perhaps recall the words or the tune. As the great fifth-century theologian St Augustine of Hippo says, "he who sings prays twice".[2] For some people with dementia

[2] St Augustine, *On the Psalms* 72.1 Martino Fine Books, 2012.

the world around them has become a noisy and agitated place. Sensitive use of music and singing, as well as careful use of silence, can evoke a sense of stillness and inner peace. Quietening the environment and creating a calm and peaceful atmosphere can help to lower stress, relieve anxiety and aid in relaxation. The time and space created through silence or subtle music may lead to surprising responses if the person is no longer bombarded with noisy distractions.

Symbols and symbolic action

Symbols are signs which point beyond themselves to a deeper meaning. So, for instance a picture of a plate, knife and fork can indicate a meal rather than just the physical plate, knife and fork.

Symbols can be material objects, movements, sounds or actions. Since they are experienced directly by the senses because they are seen, heard, tasted, touched and smelt, symbols appeal to the intuition and emotion rather than the intellect. Symbols can also build a connection with other people who share the experience and, of course with, the mystery that is God's love. Sometimes people are burdened by worries, anxieties and even guilt. Developing a simple ritual where a person can take a small pebble and give it away to God as represented by a statue or holy picture may give the person a sense of freeing, even if for only a moment.

Labels, pictures and signs can help a person negotiate life's practicalities.

However, symbols understood in this way may not always be effective for people with dementia because even signs that seem to reflect the everyday may produce hesitancy, confusion, or the person may not appreciate its association or relevance. One reason is that people simply may interpret a sign differently.

However, symbols and symbolic action that are real and tangible, rather than merely signs, can be especially helpful for people who find it difficult to express their faith in abstract terms.

Funerals

It is natural to want to shield someone living with dementia from the grief of bereavement following the death of a loved one. However, protecting them from the truth can obscure reality and cause considerable confusion, for instance when previously regular visits and phone calls no longer happen. It also means that family members must constantly coordinate and update their stories – as the person concerned might know intuitively that, "Something has happened. What is it?"

There is no single right approach to this dilemma.

Including the person in funeral arrangements and, where possible, on the day of the funeral can be a healing experience. If this is not possible, a farewell ritual on another day may be appropriate so that there is an opportunity to say their goodbyes.

Even if somebody forgets that their loved one has died, the way in which the news is communicated will remain, especially if it has been given with kindness, sensitivity and love. Although the details might not be remembered, emotions associated with factual events often remain. If any mention of the death of a loved one comes as "breaking news" and causes upset, careful handling might develop into a conversation about how much they miss and found special regarding the deceased and the good times they had shared.

Praying with people with dementia

We can always pray for people with dementia and their families, and we can pray for ourselves that we have the grace to accompany them with dignity, respect and care. Praying with people living with dementia equally asks us to be respectful. Sometimes, as Maureen tells us, prayer can come naturally.

"When Mike was still able to speak, we prayed short prayers together – the Our Father, Hail Mary, Glory Be – each morning, before we left for whatever activities were to take place that day. In his final year of life, when he was non-vocal and we were housebound, I sang the Rosary and Chaplet of Divine Mercy to him as Mike always responded better to singing. We would also watch Holy Mass from St Thomas Church in America each morning after the carers left. Throughout, I would sit close to him and Mike would stare at the images which accompanied our prayers on YouTube. It was a very calming and wonderful start to each new day."

Prayer is a practical thing that we can do and even in very advanced dementia, people may still be able to somehow respond to familiar devotions:

- use:
    - ◊ familiar prayers and scripture readings;
    - ◊ prayers discovered in dealing with the family members;

  - ◊ practical wisdom to decide what is going to work;
  - ◊ hymn-singing or symbols such as statues or the rosary;
- engage family members in these sessions as much as possible even if they do not practise or are of no faith;
- be aware of the non-verbal signs of communication that indicate, for instance, restlessness or discomfort;
- simplify prayers if necessary, especially if a response is not forthcoming;
- don't rush prayer.

Rhoda's experience with her father is a good reminder to be sensitive to the person's current reality. As Rhoda explains, "When I visit my Dad, I sometimes pray with him at the end of my visit. I must assess whether it is a good time to pray with him, because sometimes he is in the middle of other thoughts and 'happenings', so it wouldn't be suitable. For instance, he thinks he has a meeting to attend, or needs to go and tell someone something."

Rhoda also shows how to accommodate to the person's individual spirituality.

"If he is settled and we have been able to chat, then I will suggest we pray together before I leave. He was a preacher and leader in his local Evangelical church for many years, so praying is very natural to him. He will pray first (free prayer) and then I will pray afterwards. Although in normal speech he often finds it difficult to think of words, when he prays the words currently flow more naturally. This may well change as the disease progresses. Sometimes before we pray, I will offer to read to him from the Bible. I ask him where he would like me to read from. Once he said, 'Yes, but I can only cope with a few verses.' This showed his recognition that his attention can be limited at times. So, I usually read a few verses and then look up to see how he is doing before continuing and never make it too long."

However, we cannot simply assume that a person wants to pray or indeed wants to attend a religious service. The individual experience of dementia may bring about a change in the way that the person practises their faith. A person may no longer be able to read and may have forgotten the words of cherished prayers. Trying to make a person remember may cause distress. Administering spiritual care requires flexibility as responses and behaviour may be very different even from the last recent visit.

Rhoda takes a very practical viewpoint: "I am considering taking my Dad to church again soon, but I am worried that he will find it difficult to readjust as the disease has progressed and also he is increasingly incontinent. I am on a journey as to how his spiritual needs can best be met in his current situation."

Accompaniment: journeying together

As Rhoda says, we are all on a journey to understand and do our best with and for a loved one living with dementia. Hopefully, as this book has shown, people with dementia and their families and carers are not alone. Building up dementia-friendly parishes and communities is about making sure that people are accompanied on their journey: we are journeying together.

A good model for thinking about accompaniment is the story in the Gospel of St Luke of the two disciples on the road to Emmaus. The two disciples are walking away from Jerusalem, away from what they see as failure and disappointment, away from what they thought their life would be. When Jesus begins to walk with them he asks them to tell their story, "What are you discussing together as you walked along?" Jesus listens to them. One important thing here is that if we are either too far ahead or too far behind, we cannot hear what a person has to say. We must walk *with* them. Jesus engages with the disciples' worries, anxieties and pain. He stays with them because they *want* him to stay. The author, Christine Bryden, who lives with dementia, perhaps encapsulates what accompaniment means: "I may not always remember who you are, but I will always remember how you made me feel".

One question to consider, though, is who is accompanying whom? As Pope St John Paul II observed in his address about people with disabilities in St George's Cathedral in Southwark in 1982: "We begin by imagining that we are giving to them; we end by realising that they have enriched us".

Reflection for the reader:

What do you understand by accompaniment?

Has someone ever accompanied you?

Chapter 7

The sacraments

This chapter looks specifically at Catholic Canon Law and sacramental practice. However, much of what is discussed here can be applied to other Christian denominations. Even where ecclesiastical practice is different, hopefully, the theological insights that we bring to the table can be a source of fruitful dialogue in building up dementia-friendly communities.

Sacramental concerns

- Families sometimes say that their loved one:
    - ◊ receives no church visitors;
    - ◊ is not offered communion although it would be appreciated;
    - ◊ when admitting a loved one to a care home, might overlook informing the local priest or vicar. This means that:
- the parish might be unaware of someone's presence in a local care home;

  - the parish only discover someone's presence in a local care home when the family comes to discuss funeral arrangements;
  - a practising member of their church community might unintentionally not receive visits or the sacraments.
- Parish priest:
  - ◊ is obliged to know his flock "in order to fulfil his office diligently";[1]
  - ◊ has a special responsibility for helping "the sick, particularly those close to death, by refreshing them solicitously with the sacraments and commending their souls to God";[2]
  - ◊ is "at the heart of the community", so that seeking out and supporting those in "special difficulties" can inspire and develop dementia-friendly parish communities.
- Incorrect assumptions
  - ◊ There is no point in bringing the Eucharist to a person with dementia when the visit might not be remembered afterwards.
  - ◊ Giving communion to someone with dementia is inappropriate because they might no longer understand its significance.
  - ◊ Someone's manner of receiving the sacrament may be inappropriate and appear disrespectful. (However, on some occasions, this might be a correct assumption. Sometimes there can be a realistic fear that the person will spit out the Host.)

[1] *Code of Canon Law* 529 §1.

[2] *Code of Canon Law* 529 §1.

- Correct assumptions
  - ◊ Sacramental and pastoral outreach to people living with dementia is not solely about reception of the Eucharist.
  - ◊ Spiritual need permeates the sacramental and pastoral life of the Church.
  - ◊ People with "special difficulties" and people living with dementia:
    - are no different from any other member of the Church;
    - can contribute to the life of the Church "according to each one's own condition and function";[3]
    - may need carers and visitors to be innovative in their manner of spiritual support but are often fully aware of what is happening, perhaps despite appearances;
    - continue their relationship with God to the end of their lives and are still called to grow in holiness;
    - often follow and understand familiar prayers and liturgy even when finding it difficult to maintain regular contact with other aspects of life;
    - cannot be judged as unable to understand and appreciate the spiritual dimension of their lives.

Human dignity walks together with a growing faith in the knowledge and understanding of God's love.

The sacraments:

- support a personal growth in holiness;
- concern the individual personally and as part of the Church community;

[3] *Code of Canon Law* 208.

- strengthen and renew the union of the person receiving them with Christ and with the Christian community;
- raise significant questions when associated with people with dementia.

Dementia comes in many forms and stages. What is applicable in one stage may not be in another.

Someone who has dementia might have lost the ability to take full responsibility for their actions, but they still have a right to be treated with dignity, respect and with recognition of their humanity.

The manner in which a minister administers a sacrament to someone with dementia or "special needs" reflects their own personal relationship with God and the Church and their own willingness to cherish human life in all its manifestations.

A minister who values the sacraments will:

- be careful, respectful and sensitive in sharing them with someone else; [4]
- not refuse access to the sacraments to someone eligible to receive them; [5]
- consider the age as well as the social, emotional, physical, medical and psychological disposition of those who are to receive them.[6]

4 *Code of Canon Law* 840.

5 *Code of Canon Law* 843 §1.

6 *Code of Canon Law* 779.

Baptism, the "sacrament of salvation", welcomes a person into the Christian community. This means that somebody who is not baptised cannot receive the other sacraments.

Two of the sacraments – Matrimony and Holy Orders – require free choice and commitment whilst also bestowing unique responsibilities on the recipient. It is highly unlikely that a bishop would consider conferring Holy Orders on someone living with dementia.

Matrimony

Some people think about marriage when one of the couple is living with dementia. It is therefore perhaps useful to consider that the requirements for a valid marriage are:

- self-knowledge and knowledge of the one they intend to marry;
- the mental capacity and maturity to understand, appreciate and freely consent to the meaning and responsibilities of marriage;
- the ability to perform essential matrimonial rights and duties;
- the authority to make independent choices without the need of immediate direction or supervision;
- the capacity for marriage at the time of consent.

Other sacraments do not have the same requirements. A diagnosis of dementia does not stop someone freely choosing to receive the Eucharist. However, the fundamental sacrament of baptism is the gateway to the others although, at the same time, it does not confer an absolute right of access to them.[7]

Baptism: Case study

Mary and Bill have celebrated their sixtieth wedding anniversary. At the time of their wedding Mary, a committed Catholic, remembers vividly that in those days she could not have her marriage celebrated with a Catholic Mass because Bill was not a Catholic and was unbaptised. Throughout their marriage Bill always supported Mary's faith. He was happy to have their children baptised and brought up as Catholics. Sometimes he accompanied Mary to church and always had a good relationship with their priest. However, he showed no signs of wanting to become a Catholic.

Bill now has dementia and Mary has asked the priest if he will quietly baptise her husband. As she explained to the priest, "Babies can be baptised and they do not know what is going on".

Although Bill had not previously shown any indication that he wanted to become a Catholic, regardless of his current diagnosis of dementia:

- he could still change his mind;
- may have had explicit reasons for not seeking baptism;
- may or may not be judged as:
  - ◊ having implicitly considered baptism by virtue of his attendance at religious services and willingness to have his children baptised;

[7] *Code of Canon Law* 842 §1.

- ◊ capable of receiving some appropriate catechetical instruction;
- ◊ able to receive the sacraments of initiation (baptism, confirmation and the Eucharist) in a single celebration in his parish church as a member of the parish community[8] (the point here is that Mary wants to have Bill "quietly" baptised as if it is only a private matter);
- may not be baptised against his will.

However, in the case study it is not Bill but Mary who asks the priest about baptism. Bill's situation demands careful discernment by the priest.

In their teaching document *One Bread One Body,* the Catholic Bishops of England and Wales remind us that "each sacrament of the Church has its own special significance and grace", such that, "when someone receives a sacrament he or she knows and desires what the Church means by that sacrament;[9] A disability in itself is not a reason for the person to be refused baptism and an adult who intends to receive baptism is to be given catechesis that is appropriate for their situation.[10] The Good News is for everyone.

Eucharist

The theological reasoning for enabling people living with dementia to take part in the celebration of the Eucharist is both clear and profound.

[8] *Code of Canon Law* 857 §2.

[9] Catholic Bishops' Conferences of England & Wales, Ireland and Scotland *One Bread One Body, Veritas Publications* 1998, 9.

[10] *Code of Canon Law* 851.

Holy Communion either at Mass or afterwards when the Eucharist is brought to people who cannot attend Mass, is something "deeply personal, but never private".[11] As Pope St John Paul II explains," The Eucharist shows us what value each person, our brother or sister, has in God's eyes, if Christ offers himself equally to each one, under the species of bread and wine. If our Eucharistic worship is authentic, it must make us grow in awareness of the dignity of each person".[12]

Where a person has been a regular communicant there is a presumption in favour of their ability to distinguish between Holy Communion and "regular food".[13] Certainly, the ministry to bring communion to people living with dementia often requires much patience as well as practical wisdom. Here once again an understanding of dementia is vital as is the ability to work out what is happening "under the surface". Tessa's situation is a case in point.

"Every time the Eucharistic Minister came to give communion to Tessa who lived in a care home, she became tearful and refused to take the Host even though she seemed to indicate that she wanted to receive. It so happened that, on one occasion, the minister came fifteen minutes earlier than usual and found Tessa with her mid-morning break. It seemed that Tessa was refusing communion because, having just eaten, she had not observed her customary hour's fast before receiving the Eucharist. The minister discussed this with the care home staff and simply changed his routine to come at a better time for Tessa."

11 Catholic Bishops' Conferences of England & Wales, Ireland and Scotland *One Bread One Body Veritas Publications* 1998, 92.

12 Pope John Paul II, *On the Mystery and Worship of the Eucharist*, 1980, 6.

13 See the United States Conference of Catholic Bishops (USCCB), *Guidelines for the celebration of the sacraments with persons with disabilities* 2017, 26.

A person may refuse communion for a variety of reasons which may not be easy to deal with, especially where deep-seated issues seem to prevent a sense of closure or forgiveness. This is hard for many people, whether living with dementia or not. Praying with somebody, reminding them that God loves them and that Jesus is with them in a special way in the Host even if they do not feel ready to receive, can be powerful sources of comfort.

Caritas Leeds offers some useful tips on dementia and the Eucharist.[14]

- Support someone's Mass attendance for as long as possible.
- When taking communion to a person's home or to a care home create an atmosphere that helps awareness of what is happening.
- Encourage a prayerful environment.
- If the visit happens in a care home, engage staff in providing some privacy.
- When visiting someone, try to get to know them and try to find out what prayers, hymns and devotions they like.
- Try to be consistent in the days and times you visit.
- Build up relationships with the person's family, friends, those close to them and staff if the visit takes place in a care home.
- Think about the careful use of gesture, touch, tone of voice; speak slowly and carefully and be attentive to their responses.

14 Caritas Leeds, *Dementia Friendly Eucharist,* https://www.growingoldgracefully.org.uk/wp-content/uploads/2018/08/DementiaFriendlyEucharist.pdf

In this example we show a Eucharistic Minister at work.

"Clare was a member of the St Vincent de Paul Society and a Eucharistic Minister. She knew Monique, who was French, because they both attended the same Sunday and weekday Masses. Monique's husband had died some years previously and she now lived on her own, keeping herself to herself. It soon became apparent that Monique was finding Mass disorientating. She would come to Mass on her own but as soon as she arrived, she would begin to leave again. She was restless and could not sit still. At first, Clare sat next to Monique to try and help her through the service, but Clare soon realised that Monique could not relax and soon stopped coming to church. Clare arranged to pick her up but often Monique would make excuses and say she was not feeling well or had to wait in for something. After a discussion with the parish priest, it was agreed that Clare could take communion to Monique even though physically Monique could get to church."

It is worth remembering that plans to give the Eucharist to someone may have to change if, on that occasion the potential recipient may be in a particularly distressed state of mind. A quiet moment of prayer and stillness might be more appropriate than an attempt to administer the sacrament.

Notes for Eucharistic Ministers

The Eucharistic minister should consider offering a fragment of the Host to someone unable to consume a whole one.

A spoiled Host is collected in a clean cloth or tissue and disposed of according to diocesan norms, by burial, burning or dissolving it in water which is then poured, for instance, onto a flower bed.

Reconciliation

In the sacrament of reconciliation, the person asks for and obtains the mercy of God, pardon for their sins and reconciliation with the Church. It is a healing sacrament: from a psychological point of view, it can help relieve somebody's sense of guilt and sorrow; from a theological point of view, even if the person is no longer capable of sin, God's healing work continues.

Someone is only morally responsible for their own actions to the extent that they know and understand what they are doing. However, people living with dementia may still experience a sense of guilt or sorrow or be conscious of committing wrong acts.

The sacrament of reconciliation is not simply about sins and contrition but about experiencing the healing love and peace of the Lord. For people with or without dementia, this sacrament is a ministry in which those who are physically, emotionally or psychologically unwell find peace and consolation.

Sacrament of the sick

In this sacrament, the Church commends to the suffering and glorified Lord people who are seriously ill, so that he may "raise them up and save them".[15] The sacrament of the sick is for people who are close to death, in grave illness, increasing frailty and the elderly. It can be administered many times.[16] Indeed, many Catholic care homes offer their residents the sacrament a couple of times each year.

[15] Catechism of the Catholic Church, CTS, *2006* 1449.
[16] ibid. Catholic Book Publishing Corp,*1986* #11, 9.

The sacrament of the sick can be administered even if someone has lost consciousness or the use of reason, provided they would have at least implicitly asked for it when in control of their faculties. This means that unless it is certain that the person would have refused anointing, the benefit of the doubt operates and they can be given the sacrament.[17]

Further thoughts

When we listened to people living with dementia and their families, what came across clearly was the need for support. This included supporting spiritual needs and being connected to their church or faith communities. Our stories also indicated that we cannot assume that people will ask for help or support, nor can it be assumed that people will ask for their priests to visit. On the one hand we must consider this reluctance to ask for support. On the other hand, we should not simply do something without asking. This is where dementia-friendly communities become so important. In a dementia-friendly community people will not worry about asking because they know they will not be a burden or stigmatised and they know who to go to for help. As we think about how to provide support, it helps if we can tailor that support to what the person wants and needs, and make sure that support considers the person's faith practice and spiritual journey. This includes the needs, wants and journeys of family and carers. Therefore, we have tried in Chapter 6 to develop tools to help us identify a person's needs and wants, and appropriate spiritual care.

[17] ibid. #14.

When it comes to supporting people accompanying those living with dementia, faith communities are in a position of trust. This requires that accompaniers themselves are trained, dementia – aware and supported, especially in the processes of safeguarding. Moreover, the community must be prepared should the needs of accompaniers include issues around loss, grief and bereavement.

In St Luke's story of the road to Emmaus, the two disciples are so taken by the stranger's explanation of all that had happened concerning "the Christ" that they urge him to stay with them, saying "it is nearly evening, and the day is almost over". Each one of us is called to stay, to be with others, even if it is being in the silence. In that place of silence, it is the Word of God, "alive and active", that can seek out and discern the heart.[18]

Reflection for the reader:

What is your experience of accompaniment and of being accompanied?

[18] *Hebrews* 4:12-13.

Chapter 8

Becoming a dementia-friendly diocese: the case of Caritas Leeds

The Alzheimer's Society describes dementia-friendly communities as communities that encourage "everyone to share responsibility for ensuring that people with dementia feel understood, valued and able to contribute to their community."[1] Churches are at the heart of many communities and, because they are a ready-made community, they can reach out to people who are often on the margins. However, in practice, there is still work to do to ensure that churches offer a dementia-friendly environment, that services really do serve those living with dementia, and that outreach and pastoral care is effective. Above all, the church is the place where people with dementia, and their families and carers belong as full and

[1] https://www.alzheimers.org.uk/get-involved/dementia-friendly-communities

contributing members of the community. This is our story of how Caritas Leeds contributed towards Leeds becoming a dementia-friendly diocese.

Background:

Caritas Leeds, "an umbrella organisation to bring together existing social action parish groups and associations with the aim of adopting a more reflective and coordinated approach to charitable activities"[2] was formally inaugurated in September 2017. Following a diocesan audit of charitable activities and organisations, one key finding was that the elderly were carrying out substantial charitable endeavours and that people living with dementia and their carers faced challenges which were both significant and increasing.

The diocese has a long history of caring for the elderly through several religious Orders such as the Little Sisters of the Poor, through residential provision and the main diocesan charity, Catholic Care, which facilitates several community-based support groups across the diocese. There is also a separate diocesan charity, Growing Old Grace-fully, which focuses on the broader needs of the elderly, especially their spiritual care.

The Beginning

Under the auspices of Caritas Leeds, a steering group formed early in 2018 to specifically focus on the needs of people living with dementia and their carers. The steering group drew its membership from Growing Old Grace-fully, clergy, Catholic Care, an Alzheimer's Society memory support worker, carers,

2 www.dioceseofleeds.org.uk/caritas/

a person living with dementia and representatives of female religious Orders working in the diocese. The overall aim was to make the diocese more dementia-friendly. This project was guided by the Dementia Action Alliance (Yorkshire and Humberside) standards, but the aim was also to champion ways of enhancing the spiritual aspects of people living with dementia and their carers.

Group discussions drew upon their experiences in discerning the status quo in our diocese.

The thousands of people who attend our churches each week include a significant number of people who are living with dementia and their carers. Some clergy and laity involved in the care of older people are consulting with people living with dementia to ensure their voice is heard and their needs are met in all our parishes. We therefore needed to capture these voices because people living with dementia have much to teach us.

Our diocese has seen inspiring parish responses which include a monthly memory Mass, memory cafes and activity groups that enable those with dementia to fulfil their pastoral and spiritual needs.

Our vision is to develop and enhance these responses, as well as to create more in-depth resources to explore and highlight good spiritual care. Yet there are still many misunderstandings about dementia and parishes have a huge role to play in helping people to live well with dementia.

We all need to work towards being more dementia-friendly so that everyone feels they are not just included in parish life, but also that they really belong. Being acknowledged by the Dementia Alliance and having use of their logo is not just a badging exercise. Neither is being a dementia-friendly diocese just a title: it has the potential to make a big difference to families within the Catholic community and beyond.

The steering group considered initiatives started by others such as the Diocese of Nottingham, the Archdiocese of Liverpool, the Diocese of Middlesbrough and the Alzheimer Society Friendly Church Guide. This fruitful exercise culminated in our own first action plan. This included the following points.

1. To make the Alzheimer's Society Dementia Friends awareness programme available in all our parish communities.

2. To include the Dementia Friends awareness session in the training of key personnel such as Extraordinary Ministers of the Eucharist, students for the permanent diaconate, members of the St Vincent de Paul Society and others.

3. To make accessible more in-depth resources for key personnel to help in ensuring that the practice of faith and spiritual needs are acknowledged and met.

4. To review the pastoral care of diocesan priests and religious living with dementia, an aspect of the work carried out by Catholic Care.

Each goal had specific tasks, a target date and a review section. This plan was reviewed after twelve months in October 2019, resulting in the following revised action points.

1. To continue with increasing the number of dementia friendly sessions at parish level but to review our strategy for achieving this.

2. To develop formal links with other agencies associated with the care of people living with dementia and their carers such as Christians on Ageing, a national organisation.

3. To seek the views and experience of clergy and religious in our diocese regarding what would help them in ministering to people living with dementia

4. To explore links with an academic from Leeds University who is looking at the issue of decision-making and people living with dementia.

5. To explore links with the Leeds Teaching Hospital NHS Trust Chaplaincy, especially with their Faith and Frailty forum which includes NHS staff, Leeds City Council and chaplains of various faiths.

Resources

As a result of both action plans, initiatives and on-line practical resources targeted three main stakeholders: lay faithful, carers and clergy/religious.

Lay Faithful

- A brief paper about dementia which offers context and helpful hints on how to engage with people living with dementia.
- *Visiting people with dementia:* a practical generic resource.

- *Praying with people living with dementia:* to help family members or visitors from the parish.
- *Dementia-Friendly Eucharist:* to support the work of extra-ordinary ministers of the Eucharist when visiting people living with dementia at home or in care homes.
- Generic resource about dementia and the sacraments of the sick and reconciliation.
- *What is a Dementia Friend?:* to encourage individuals or parish groups to raise awareness about dementia.

Carers

- A personal account of a wife caring for her husband living with dementia.
- Short version of the Diocesan Transport Policy.
- *Directory of Organisations,* offering support to people living with disabilities within the boundary of our diocese, which includes dementia.
- Direct link to the free and easy to access services offered by the Alzheimer's Society, offering personalised support and advice service for people living with all types of dementia, their families and carers.
- For two consecutive years we held a thirty-minute Dementia-friendly carol service consisting of familiar carols, readings, short prayers and a get-together afterwards. Both services included a children's choir. One non-English carol acknowledged the cultural diversity of the Leeds diocese.

Clergy and Religious

- Input into clergy conferences and communications through the *Ad Clerum* promoted materials produced by the group.
- Input on dementia during a day-workshop on mental health challenges to their ministry.
- Inclusion of dementia challenges during a day-workshop on human dignity.
- Dementia and the healing sacrament of reconciliation for the clergy.
- Mass toolkit to make Mass and other liturgies more accessible and inclusive.
- Resources for clergy and Religious on ministering to people living with dementia which include personal testimonies and stories, theological perspectives, prayers, meditations and practical approaches.

All of the above resources are accessible online:
www.dioceseofleeds.org.uk/caritas/our-resources/ and
www.dioceseofleeds.org.uk/caritas/dementia-friendly-forum/

Challenges

As one would realistically expect, getting to this point was not without its challenges.

It was important to hear the voice of people living with dementia. We drew upon the experiences of people working with this client group, including a very well-informed carer on the steering group who shared her experience of looking after her husband.

Despite the bishop's encouragement, two simple questionnaires which asked diocesan clergy and Religious about their ministry support needs received a low response rate.

Determined to continue working towards our overall goal through our action plan, we also used the *Ad Clerum* as a means of seeking views and communicating progress with our initiatives.

Unfortunately, the covid pandemic restricted our 2020 plans to mark Dementia Awareness Week and Disabilities Week. However, in the summer of 2021 we held a virtual event under the title of Dementia: Awareness and Action. This focused on human dignity and included a Pentecost-inspired liturgy, testimonials and discussions on faith and dementia-related themes. An edited version of the event can be accessed through the Caritas Leeds website, dementia group section.

To where from here?

If your parish or community is thinking about how to become dementia-friendly here are some things you may wish to consider.[3]

1. Discuss what a dementia-friendly and a dementia-unfriendly church might look like.

2. Think about your current outreach to people with dementia and their families, and note where there are gaps.

3 Caritas Social Action Network is a good resource for finding out more: https://welcome-me-as-i-am.thinkific.com/courses/take/its-still-me-lord/texts/2406794-see-me-rather-than-dementia

3. List some of the training you think you need.
4. Talk to other churches and organisations so that you can learn from each other's experiences.
5. Think about issues such as safeguarding, and the legal and ethical aspects of care.

Reflection for the reader:

Do you belong to a dementia-friendly community?

If you do, how does this work for you?

If you don't, what else do you need to set one up?

Chapter 9

Concluding reflections

When we started this project, our central aim was to offer a resource that could accompany people living with dementia, their families and carers, pastoral workers and communities. We wanted this resource to help people to live well with dementia. Dying well is a part of living well.

To help people to live and die well with dementia requires tools, skills and sharing experience, but all of this is futile without one major resource – listening to the voices of people who are living this reality. Therefore, from the beginning right through to the end, we have tried to be truly attentive to what people have told us.

In this last chapter we reflect on what we have learned from this project with a view, not only to record what we have heard, but also and more specifically, to act on this so that we can become, individually and together, better listening and inclusive churches and communities. This process and what we have learned fit neatly into a method identified in Catholic Social Teaching, the see, judge, act method. And as Justin Welby, Anglican Archbishop of Canterbury, says in his book *Reimagining Britain,* the values and aims of Catholic Social Teaching can be the source for fruitful reflection for all Christians.[1]

See, judge, act

Rooted in the Gospels, the see, judge, act method is well known to Catholic Social Teaching and dates from at least the thirteenth century and St Thomas Aquinas.

To see

To see well we need to know about the basics of dementia and its progression. We are not required to become experts but we do have a responsibility to be aware of the essentials and know where to ask for advice.

For Pope Francis, to "see" is to journey together towards understanding reality with the eyes of faith and heart of God. If we want to see well, we must hear the voices of people living with dementia and of their families. Seeing and hearing involves different levels of awareness: the individual person living with dementia, the family, the parish and the community.

To judge

Pope Francis says that judging should be about the situation, not the people involved. Every human being is a child of God

[1] Justin Welby, *Reimagining Britain:* foundations for hope (London: Bloomsbury, 2021), 40-42.

and our brother or sister. Regardless of their condition, each is a unique and irreplaceable person endowed with full human dignity. Our judgements, therefore, should engage theological reflection, mercy and compassion in the light of truth. In this way, we are better equipped to discern situations and judge what should be our action.

Judging is not about "them" and "us" evaluation and inclusivity on our terms. We start from the premise that everyone has a place and a contribution to make, and this does not rely on "us" making "room" for "them". Individually and as groups such as clergy, Religious, church welcomers, catechists, Eucharistic Ministers and community helpers, we must learn more and know more about dementia. We may also need to alter our outlook, attitudes and approach so that we can truly accompany people and enable them to live well.

Judging allows us to discern the lights and shadows of living with dementia in a way that does not obscure how we see the person as someone loved for themselves, by others and by God.

To act

Listening and discerning are effective when, inspired by prayer, faith and hope, they are accompanied by careful planning and converted into action.

Action has many aspects.

- It aims at eradicating discrimination and stigma of dementia by informing people about how we can live well with dementia.

- It puts in place practical strategies to minimise difficulties and maximise opportunities to live well.
- It is related to theology. People living with dementia are as capable as anybody else of helping to spread the Good News of God's love. They may just do so differently from their earlier days.

Dementia and dignity

The stories we have listened to in this book show time and again how people living with dementia and their families witness to the full dignity of the human person.

Catholic Social Teaching recognises that each of us, regardless of our status and personal circumstances, is made in God's image and has an innate human dignity which nobody has the right to deny or take away. Dignity does not depend on the actions or attitudes of others and cannot be reduced to autonomy or intellectual capacities.

The placing of people in undignified situations is not limited to people with dementia and is often related to discrimination, stigma and uncaring or ignorant attitudes. However, even in undignified situations, especially when this involves personal and intimate care, people never lose their right to be recognised and treated with dignity and respect. Therefore, in our stories, our contributors frequently speak, not about "suffering with" dementia, but about "living with" and living "well" with the condition.

Our stories show that those who live with dementia love and are loved by others. They depend on other people and our many dementia voices witness to the significance of such trust. To be able to entrust yourself, often totally, into the care of others is to reveal an important aspect of our humanity: that we can believe that other people have our best interests at heart.

Everyone has a part to play in building up dementia-friendly communities in a beautiful act of solidarity for the common good. That is why this book aims to help someone living with dementia to do as much as they can for as long as they can, offering our support as and when it's needed. It's about recognising their unique value and dignity, regardless of their circumstances. Cherishing a person's rights to independence, privacy and to have a say in their own present and future allows them to continue as loved and loving family and community members. Their unique gifts and talents still contribute to their happiness, wellbeing and relationships whilst enriching the people around them.

People with dementia are neither statistics nor potential sacrificial victims on the altar of expediency for the wider population's convenience. Declining abilities do not make someone a "drain on resources" or any less worthy of respect and dignity. If anything, increasing vulnerability makes someone even more worthy of our love as they teach us, through our care, how to become more fully human, more fully alive. Through someone's dementia, we learn the complex and deeper meaning of what it means to live in the present and of being dependent, interdependent and fragile beings, loved by a loving God who is concerned for "the least, the last and the lost". [2]

2 www.dioceseofleeds.org.uk/caritas/foreword-from-bishop-marcus/#.

The last words

We hope that our book contributes to the conversation to enable people with dementia to live well and fully, individually and in community. By breaking down barriers through our dementia voices, we hope that people will feel more able to share their diagnosis in the knowledge that they will be supported and heard; that they will not only be welcomed in dementia-friendly churches and communities but be encouraged to participate and share their individual and unique contributions to those communities. We hope that our communities will develop beyond adjusting and creating accessibility to growing into genuinely inclusive rather than exclusive communities. We hope that we have provided voices at the service of the Church and our communities that can identify unmet needs, help in the provision of resources, and not only listen further to people's voices but also act on these voices. We trust that sharing our practice and sharing both the realities of pain and joy in people's journeys will contribute to a way forward that is inspired by hope.